Literature of Mystery and Detection

This is a volume in the Arno Press collection

Literature of Mystery and Detection

See last page of this volume
for a complete list of titles

AUTOBIOGRAPHY

OF A

FRENCH DETECTIVE

FROM

1818 TO 1858

[Louis] Canler

ARNO PRESS
A New York Times Company
1976

Editorial Supervision: EVE NELSON

Reprint Edition 1976 by Arno Press Inc.

Reprinted from a copy in
The University of Illinois Library

LITERATURE OF MYSTERY AND DETECTION
ISBN for complete set: 0-405-07860-9
See last pages of this volume for titles.

Manufactured in the United States of America

Library of Congress Cataloging in Publication Data

Canler, Louis, 1797-1865.
Autobiography of a French detective, from 1818 to 1858.

(Literature of mystery and detection)
Translation of Mémoires de Canler.
Reprint of the 1862 ed. published by Ward and Lock, London.
1. Canler, Louis, 1797-1865. 2. Police--France--Correspondence, reminiscences, etc. I. Title.
II. Series.
HV7911.C35A3313 1976 363.2'092'4 [B] 75-32738
ISBN 0-405-07866-8

AUTOBIOGRAPHY

OF A

FRENCH DETECTIVE

FROM

1818 TO 1858

COMPRISING

THE MOST CURIOUS REVELATIONS OF THE FRENCH
DETECTIVE POLICE SYSTEM

BY

M. CANLER
Ancien Chef du Service de Sûreté

LONDON
WARD AND LOCK, 158, FLEET STREET
MDCCCLXII.

LONDON:
SAVILL AND EDWARDS, PRINTERS, CHANDOS-STREET,
COVENT GARDEN.

PREFACE.

If this book possess no other attraction, it has at least the merit of offering to English readers the true and ungarbled experiences of a French detective police officer, from 1818 to 1858. The comparison afforded by these revelations with our police system, so admirably described in the "Experiences of a Real Detective,"* is, to my mind, highly instructive, although I am sorry to find that in both countries more value appears to be set on the detection than on the prevention of crime.

It is not surprising to find that M. Canler's work has passed through three editions in a fortnight, for such books are scarce. At the end of that period, however, the French Government has thought it advisable to suppress the work; for what reason seems inexplicable, except that the authorities may feel

---

* "Shilling Volume Library," No. 23.

rather ashamed of the Revelations which Canler does not hesitate to make about the working of the Police system in France, which countenances criminals in the hope that they may betray their companions. However this may be, Canler's work is no longer to be read in French, and a very curious peep-hole into a strange state of things has been arbitrarily closed. Fortunately, I secured my copy prior to the prohibition; and not being subject to the restraint of the Comte de Persigny's dictum, I have done my best to make a most remarkable and suggestive volume known to the English public.

LASCELLES WRAXALL.

WEST BROMPTON,
August, 1862.

AUTOBIOGRAPHY

OF A

FRENCH DETECTIVE.

CHAPTER I.

THE FRENCH DETECTIVES.

BEFORE I begin to record my experiences during the forty years in which I was engaged in the French police force, I consider it right to say a few words as to the origin of the detective system existing in Paris.

In 1810, the notorious Vidocq was in Bicêtre prison, awaiting with other galley-slaves the departure of the chain-gang with which he would return to the hulks whence he had escaped. To this man, who was gifted with a vivid imagination and an ardent temperament, the thought of captivity was very painful, and as he had on several occasions acted as denunciator, in the baseness of his heart he hit on a method to improve his condition, even if he did not regain his liberty.

He, therefore, offered to act as spy in the prisons, that is to say, gain the confidence of his comrades and make them confess their crimes. At the same time he sent in a report about several convicts who had escaped or broken their bars, and were detained at Bicêtre under false names. Lastly, he gave such precise information about certain daring robbers, who had for a long time been infesting the capital, as led to their arrest.

At this period, detective police did not exist, or more correctly speaking, existed under conditions which rendered them almost of no effect. The police officers, entirely independent of each other, acted as they thought proper in their own district, and a robber who was hunted down in one quarter could carry on his trade with impunity in another. Vidocq's reports were examined and verified, and the Prefect of police thought that such a man would be invaluable as a spy; he was therefore employed in that capacity at Bicêtre and La Force, receiving pay proportioned to the importance of the captures which he helped to effect. M. Henry at length resolved to set him at liberty, on condition that he should act as denouncer, and each month supply the prefecture with a settled minimum of criminals, under penalty of being sent back to Brest himself; he had a fixed salary of four pounds a month, and a premium for each arrest.

One of the first arrests which Vidocq effected was that of a leather-dresser, who had given him a shelter when he left prison, and whom he accused, justly or unjustly, of being a coiner. The leather-dresser was arrested, with a surgeon who was a friend of his ; they were condemned and executed, as a reward for the hospitality granted to the pensioner of the police. Vidocq's perfidy had been too lucrative for him to remain idle ; fear on one side, cupidity on the other, endowed him with incredible activity, and in order not to fall below his minimum of arrests, he resolved to have recourse to provocation, and employed this ignoble scheme with the most criminal skill up to the return of the Bourbons, when he thought it would be more profitable to offer his services to the royalists. He it was who had the honour of dragging down the statue of Napoleon I. from the column on the Place Vendôme.

In 1817, when the political excitement had grown calmer, Vidocq was given a dozen agents of his own stamp to hunt down criminals, and it was only from this date that he was chief of the detective staff. In 1821, the number of agents was increased to twenty-one, and secret funds were placed at the disposal of the ex-galley-slave, for which he did not account. What could be expected from men of this character? what esteem could be felt for a service thus constituted? Public opinion very naturally classified the detectives with the criminals, and Vidocq's axiom "set a thief to catch a thief," was the truth, because he always selected of preference, the most daring criminals as his assistants. Of course, such a staff often deceived their chief, as the following instance will show :—

A stranger, who gave the name of Jacquin, offered his services to Vidocq as a spy.

"What can you do?" the policeman asked.

"A good many things," the other replied. "For instance, I am a splendid hand at a bargain. Just try me."

"Very good. Take these two five-franc pieces, and go and buy me a couple of fowls. I am curious to see your choice."

The stranger promised to return shortly, and in fact soon handed Vidocq two splendid chickens, as well as the ten francs he had received to purchase them with.

"Very good," said the master; "but tell me how you managed it."

"In this way," Jacquin answered. "I borrowed a white jacket, cap, and basket from a friend of mine who is a scullion. I filled my basket with stones, which I covered over with some vegetables I bought, and I then went and paid my court, as a polite cook, to a woman selling fowls. I made a bargain with her, and paid her. My basket was heavy, and I had it on my back, and not caring to take it off to put the fowls in it, I asked the good woman to be kind enough to do so. I stood facing her, as is but proper when dealing with the fair sex, and stooped down. While her hands were engaged above my head, mine were busy in the large front pocket of her apron. It is really a strange custom of these women to place their takings on their stomach. I felt delicately in the pocket, without tickling her, and took back my own coins, as well as these thirty francs."

"Do you often work like that?" Vidocq asked.

"A man must do what he can," the other answered.

"Modest, and not clumsy! Very well; I will take you into my service from to-morrow. So mind and do not get into trouble between this and then."

And Vidocq dismissed the man. While Jacquin was showing him how he did the trick, he had made plenty of gesticulations and movements. He had stooped and bent his knee, in order to realize the scene: without failing in deference, he had several times touched his examiner, but he turned his gestures to good account, for he cleverly robbed Vidocq of a valuable gold watch and appendages. Jacquin, if that were his name, thought it as well not to return the next day. Vidocq, whose anger and vanity were unexpectedly aroused, made every effort to discover the clever thief, but neither the watch nor Jacquin was ever found again; and for many years after this fact no agent cared to mention his name in Vidocq's presence.

In 1827 Vidocq resigned office, and retired with a fortune, which certainly was not produced by his savings from his salary. Foreseeing that, sooner or later, the authorities would feel a reluctance to employ him, Vidocq started a paper manufactory at St. Mandé, and assumed the management on his retirement; but with a name like his it was difficult for him to establish respectable commercial relations. Hence he sold his factory, and lived privately till the beginning of 1832, at which period political troubles disturbed the capital. He then contrived to impress the prefect of police with the idea that his services would be necessary, and obtained leave to establish a secret detective police. For this purpose, he opened an office, and engaged the services of several notorious characters like himself. Once reinstalled, the ex-convict had but one thought, that of regaining his place as head of the detective branch; but for this purpose he required some brilliant stroke. He induced one of his followers, by dazzling promises, to "put up" a robbery, and his victims were arrested just as they were breaking into a house.

In consequence of such a capture, which seemed due to the skilful vigilance of Vidocq, and at the same time proved the relative inferiority of his successor in office, the authorities thought it right, shortly after, to restore Vidocq to his old post. The robbers were brought before the magistrates, and unanimously declared that they had engaged in the burglary at the instigation of L—— that is to say, Vidocq's agent, and a warrant for his arrest was issued. But this did not suit Vidocq, who feared lest his agent might confess, and hence he impudently declared that L—— was not to be found. Four months later, the magistrate was secretly informed that Vidocq had placed L—— in his brigade under the assumed name of Auguste, and he was forced to give him up much against his will. At the assizes the five robbers, were condemned to penal servitude, and L—— to two years' imprisonment, as putter-up of the burglary.

From the moment that Vidocq resumed his duties, the judges were sorely offended by the prisoners' objections to the evidence of the detectives; and such recriminations produced the worst effect upon the spectators. In fact the depositions of the agents called as witnesses were constantly interrupted by the prisoners, who accused them of being their old comrades at the hulks, or even accomplices in the robbery to which they bore witness. In spite of these recriminations and this scandal, however, matters went on in the same way till extraneous circumstances put an end to this police system, which was universally disapproved. The revolution of 1830 produced freedom of the press, and the newspapers freely made use of it by inserting caricatures in which Vidocq was represented side by side with an august personage. Insulted by these odious comparisons, for which the official position of the ex-convict furnished a pretext, the Minister of the Interior ordered the Prefect of Police to dissolve the Detective brigade, and recompose it on an entirely new basis, of men bearing an irreproachable character. This took place on November 15, 1832, and the head-quarters of the new force were established at No. 5, Rue de Jerusalem. The new Detective brigade consisted of one chief, one principal inspector, four sergeants, twenty inspectors, and five clerks—forming a total of thirty-one members.

M. Allard was appointed head of the department and myself principal inspector, and I was ordered to pick up agents among the Sergents de Ville and other persons unconnected with the service.

This measure was healthy, but at the same time an evil result might be apprehended: Vidocq's agents, finding themselves suddenly deprived of their means of livelihood, might return to their first mode of life—namely, robbery; and these half-converted men must be prevented at any price from relapsing into crime. It was therefore decided that they should be retained as indicators, have a room in town at which to meet, and receive in addition to a salary of fifty francs a month, a reward for every arrest effected through their exertions. Only fourteen accepted this offer.

Having thus cleared the ground, I will now begin the history of my connexion with the police force.

CHAPTER II.

HOW I JOINED THE POLICE.

My father, after serving in the campaigns of the Republic up to 1796, was transferred as sergeant to a company of Veterans at St. Omer, where I was born on April 4, 1797. In 1801, my father was appointed acting governor of the military gaol at Namur, and I thus spent my earliest years in a prison. The recollections of that period have made me understand what influence the impressions of youth have upon the ideas which are developed at a later date in the man. Brought up in principles of the strictest probity, I naturally felt a salutary terror of everything that might entail punishment. Hence, when I recal my childhood, and consider the part I performed in my riper years, I cannot help being struck by the relation that exists between the instruction of my early years and the career I afterwards selected.

When I was eight years of age, the Emperor came to inspect the Namur garrison, and my father handed in a petition asking for my appointment as drummer. This was graciously conceded, and I joined the service on June 18, 1805. I need not dwell at any length on my military career; suffice it to say, that I was stationed at Antwerp in the memorable siege which Carnot sustained against the Allies, and also fought at Quatre-bras and Waterloo. After the Restoration I was quartered with my regiment at Paris, where I married in 1817, and obtained my final discharge at Havre on December 31, 1818.

I returned to Paris, but in order to live in that city a man must either have a situation or private property, and I possessed neither. Truth to tell, I did not know exactly what I was fit for; but I resolved to learn a trade. I therefore went as apprentice to a paper-stainer, and though I ground colours, went errands, and often returned home at night with one cheek red the other green, I would have willingly endured my lot had I not had continually to put up with the abuse and insults of my coarse master. Disgusted with the trade I gave it up.

A few months after leaving the factory I noticed, while passing through the Rue Sebastian, a large crowd assembled in front of a house. I went up, and heard that a person lodging on the third floor of the house had found in his room a thief, busily engaged in rifling him; that when he tried to collar the scoundrel the latter threatened him with a large knife; and that the lodger then ran off to fetch the guard, after having the presence of mind to turn the key in the door.

"I really believe," my informant added, "that it will be all of no use; and that, when the guard arrives, the villain will have escaped by the chimney."

"In that case," I exclaimed, "there is no time to lose; he must be arrested at once."

And without waiting for an answer I rushed into the house, made the porter follow me, and bidding him show me the room, I dashed in; but the cage was empty—the bird had flown. I ran to the chimney, which I found my man climbing up with the aid of his hands and knees. In a second I pulled off the mattresses, and tore out of the paillasse a few handfuls of straw, which I threw into the fireplace, and set fire to. The flames had scarce began to ascend, when I heard a hoarse voice crying to me, "Stop, for mercy sake; do not make any more fire. I will come down; the smoke is stifling me." Directly after, we heard the robber really coming; but as I thought that he might feel inclined to use his knife, I stood inside the chimney, and so soon as his legs were within reach I seized them, and pulling them violently, brought him down like a sack, and fell upon him. I deprived him very soon of his knife; and the porter helped me to hold him till the guard arrived, and took him off to the police-station. He was tried at the assizes, and sentenced to seven years' penal servitude.

This affair gave me the idea of devoting myself to the pursuit of criminals; and for this purpose I applied to the prefect of police for a situation, which was given me shortly after the assassination of the Duc de Berry.

At the time when I joined, the duties of the police were of a political, much more than a magisterial nature, and the celebrated "Congregation" employed every effort, even terrorism, to induce Louis XVIII. to revoke the charter, and re-establish an absolute government. Hence arose the atrocious system of "provocative agents," whose duty it was to draw innocent persons into plots against the Government, which served the double purpose of intimidating the king, and displaying the activity and zeal of the police. At the same time I may mention that while no agent had a chance of promotion unless he attended mass and confessed regularly, the amount of corruption among the police was frightful; and I have no doubt that the system of provocation fostered it to a considerable extent. Some instances of this provocation may not be out of place here.

Two police agents were sent into Southern France, ostensibly to sell portraits and plaster busts of the members of the royal family; but they also had in their pedlars' pack engravings and small leaden statuettes, representing the Emperor, and secretly sold to amateurs. If any imprudent man let himself be caught by this species of political smuggling, the two agents, who were provided with special recommendations to the local authorities, immediately denounced the delinquent. His house was searched, the prohibited object was inevitably found, and the owner was very soon tried, and condemned.

In Paris, the provocation was effected in various ways. Honest workmen, attracted to wine-shops by men who called themselves their brothers, wore the same dress, and spoke the same language, were excited by wine to utter a remark against the Government. Gradually confidence was established : they eventually raised their voices and abused those in power, the king himself, perhaps ; hence they were naturally led to manifest a desire for a radical change, and at the instigation of the crafty agents they joined in an illusory plot which was never to see light. Under the influence of intoxication they signed a compact drawn up among the bottles. So soon as this was secured by the agent, he deposited it at the prefecture, and one fine morning the hapless dupe of this villany woke up in a cell.

To give an idea of the execrable means employed by the police, I will devote a chapter to a few of the machinations which came under my own cognizance; and for this purpose will select some cases in which the Congregation was mixed up, and others in which the police worked for their own profit.

CHAPTER III.

PROVOCATIVE AGENTS.

When the Duc de Berry, the last descendant of a race which seemed on the point of expiring, died under Louvois' knife, he had the consolation of learning that the Duchess was *enceinte.* The newspapers announced the fact, and the royalists did not fail to remark that the instigator of the murder had hoped to deprive the king of a direct successor, but that Heaven marvellously interposed to foil his plans. Still, this hope did not delight everybody; and three persons, Gravier, ex-officer of the Empire, Bouton, and L——, resolved to produce a miscarriage on the part of the Duchess by exploding petards under the windows of her bedroom. Once the plan was formed, the conspirators set to work, Bouton and Gravier undertaking to buy the gunpowder and make the instrument requisite for the crime. But these two men soon began to feel alarm and remorse, they saw the deed they meditated in all its horror; the affair began to drag, and they would probably have given up all thought of it, had there not been a Judas who had already sold the blood of his accomplices.

L—— had been for some time in direct relation with peace-officer Rivoire, whom he saw daily at the Prefecture; he was perfectly known to all the agents, but had the wit to conceal from them the names of those whom he was betraying, while promising to give them up at the moment when they were committing the crime. Bouton and Gravier were daily visited by their false brother, and he continually urged them to finish the two bombshells. When this was done L—— and Gravier proceeded on the night of April 29th to the vicinity of the Tuileries, and exploded the first shell, which, however, produced no result. Bouton and Gravier were so affected by this criminal attempt that they resolved to give up their culpable plans, but L—— having charged them with cowardice, his two dupes let themselves be guided by the villain, and it was decided that they should explode the second bomb on the night of May 6th.

At the appointed hour, L—— accompanied Gravier to the gate of the Tuileries in the Rue de Rivoli, but managed when he reached the gate to slip away. At the moment when Gravier stooped down to deposit the bomb, Rivoire and his agents seized him, and Bouton was arrested shortly after. In their examination the two prisoners alluded to their accomplice, and the police, who did not wish him to be caught, sent him off to Holland, where he spent the money which he had earned by his treachery. As for Gravier and Bouton they were sentenced to death, but the Duchess de Berry wrote a letter to the king, her uncle, imploring mercy for them; and their sentence was commuted into penal servitude for life.

Beranger's songs, which were prohibited, but which, in spite of that, were sung everywhere, caused the Congregation intense annoyance; the police agents were, therefore, ordered to employ all possible means to seize these songs at the booksellers' shops. The agent D——, for the sake of pleasing his superiors in this affair, went to M. Terry, a publisher in the Palais Royal; he stated that he was a shipper to the United States, that he had a vessel nearly ready to start, and that all he was waiting for was several thousand copies of Beranger's songs; if M. Terry could supply him with them he would pay liberally. The publisher, who had not got them, declared the thing impossible, but D—— pressed him so closely, that M. Terry at length agreed to procure them for him from another bookseller's firm. The hour was arranged for their delivery at a false address, given by D——, who ordered three of his colleagues to watch the publisher, and at the moment when the latter was going to D——'s lodgings with the copies, he was arrested in the street. The unhappy man was condemned to six months' imprisonment, and a heavy fine.

As we see, provocation was quite the regular thing, but what appears at the first blush not only surprising but incomprehensible, is the great number of manufacturers and tradesmen duped by the scoundrels, for the agents exercised but very slight powers of imagination in getting them into their nets. The same means were repeatedly employed; orders for busts of Napoleon, tricolour cockades, in a word seditious objects intended, according to their showing, for shipment to the United States or the minor American Republics. Still there was no lack of warnings; the newspapers daily announced condemnations for the sale or manufacture of prohibited objects; but the thirst for gain daily produced fresh infractions.

Such a system could only excite the evil passions of certain agents, for there was but one way of attracting the notice of the superior officers, discovering a conspiracy or a plot, or, if after lengthened search nothing were discovered, cleverly forming some infamous machination, inculpating in some pretended plot an honest father of a family, who had never dreamed of conspiring, and denouncing him to the police.

It was on this latter method that one B——, a peace-officer attached to M. Delavau, decided. This man was endowed with remarkable energy; as cunning as he was enterprising, he managed to profit by everything, and, as he was devoured by an inordinate ambition, he sought every opportunity to prove his value.

One morning he sent for an agent of the name of D——, a tailor by trade, and ex-Garde Royal, who wore the decoration of the Legion of Honour. "My good fellow," he said to him, so soon as they were alone, "they say at the Prefecture that we are doing nothing; it is true that for some time past no important operation has been effected, and so it is indispensable that we should restore ourselves in the opinion of the authorities, by proving what we are capable of. I thought of you, for I know your skill and intelligence, and I am persuaded that if I entrust the affair to you, you will bring it to a successful end."

(Here D—— grinned, and made a polite bow.)

"To-morrow morning," the peace-officer continued, "you will go to some wholesale dealer in the Rue St. Denis, being careful to select one well known for his liberal opinions, and order several dozen pairs of tricolour braces; this can be easily passed off as a charming little conspiracy, for, instead of receiving the braces, we will simply have them seized."

Provided with these instructions, D—— strolled about the Rue St. Denis with his hands in his pockets, seeking among all the names above the shop-fronts the one which he had better select. The next morning he called on M. Burth, a manufacturer of braces, who, as he was informed, was a liberal.

"I am, sir," he said to him, "shipping agent to several American republics, which all require just at present tricolour braces."

"I sincerely regret," the tradesman replied, "that I cannot supply you ; I do not sell tricolour braces, and cannot and dare not take any such order. I have braces here of all sorts and sizes ; if they suit you I shall be happy to make a bargain with you."

D—— declined, and went with hangdog looks to inform his superior officer of his ill-success.

"My good fellow," the latter said, impatiently, "I really feel sorry for you, for I entrusted you with a superb affair and you have spoiled it. Well, you must get out of the scrape as best you can, for I spoke about the matter this very morning, and it must succeed, no matter how !"

D—— promised to carry the splendid affair out, and for this purpose returned to Burth.

"I have reflected, sir," he said to him, "and as it is impossible for you to execute my order, I shall probably find the same difficulties elsewhere ; I have, therefore, made up my mind to do the best I can with the braces which you have to sell."

Then he selected and bought several dozen pairs of perfectly white braces, which all bore the manufacturer's trade mark, after which he went home and spent the night in edging these braces with blue and red ribbon, and they thus became tricolour.

The next morning he went to M. B——'s office with the braces, a warrant was issued, and M. Burth's shop and house were searched. This search, of course, led to no discovery, but for all that the tradesman was arrested, and released a few days after for want of sufficient evidence. Some time later, M. Burth went to the Théâtre Français, when to his surprise he saw the braces purchaser talking with one of the officials, and D——, on seeing him, in his turn, disappeared.

The tradesman, who had a secret grudge against the man who had tricked him and nearly got him into an awkward scrape, inquired who he was, and learned that he was D——, the police-agent. The next day he sent in a complaint, and the public prosecutor commenced an inquiry which led to no result, as it could not be expected that a police-agent would be convicted.

In order to satisfy public opinion, which was aroused by this trick, the infamy of which the newspapers described in the fullest details, D—— was officially discharged, but a short time later restored; and M. Burth was again cheated, for, while he was congatulating himself on having punished the scoundrelly provoker, the ex-tailor did not even lose a single day's pay.

The last instance I will record is of a more tragical nature. After the dismissal of the Decazes Ministry, the king entrusted the government to Simeon, a semi-liberal, who did too much or too little to conciliate everybody, and while the liberals declared that he impeded progress, he alienated the ultras by insignificant concessions. The latter, therefore, employed every method to induce the king to dismiss Simeon and put in his place men known for their royalism and devotion to the Jesuits; but as all their intrigues produced no result they resolved to try a grand stroke by which to overcome what they called the king's obstinacy, and imagined an infernal expedient. They selected for its execution a man of no character, of the name of N——, who had lost his whole fortune at play, and belonged body and soul to the Congregation.

On January 29th, 1821, a small barrel, containing three or four pounds of gunpowder, was placed on the landing of the back stairs leading to the apartments of the Duchesse d'Angoulême. It was hidden in a wash basket, and had a sulphur match, which N—— fired at a quarter to five in the evening, and then hurried from the Tuileries. A few seconds after, the explosion took place with such violence that all the window panes were broken.

The police at once went to the château to commence their inquiry, and, as may be easily supposed, the noble instigators of this frightful attempt were not the last to go to the magistrates; and all their manœuvres tended to throw the odium of the affair and the proof of culpability upon "the enemies of the throne and the altar, the liberals."

I went to the Tuileries with peace-officer Dabasse, and followed the affair through all the details. In spite of their formal denials, tears, and entreaties, two unhappy Savoyard lads, who had swept a chimney near the king's study on the previous day, were taken to the Prefecture; and though scarce ten years of age, were cross-questioned in every possible way, but their sole reply was, "we know nothing about a barrel, and do not understand what you mean." When confined in the Prefecture, they were placed in separate rooms, with an agent appointed to each to make him speak and confess his share in the crime.

It was supposed that these poor lads, bribed by some obstinate enemy of the Bourbons, had consented to convey the barrel into the palace, unconscious of the importance of the deed. The agent, Froment, who was anything but patient, and who was imprisoned with the elder lad, grew tired of this life, and asked leave to go out for a few hours, promising to return in the evening; but he was expected in vain. It was then feared that he had drawn the secret from the boy, and gone to warn the conspirators, and obtain from them a reward proportionate to the danger of the revelation he might have made. The Prefect at once issued a warrant against Froment, who was only found on the third day, and locked up with the boy for a week; after which period they were all liberated, as justice had laid hands on the real culprit. N— was arrested.

This arrest singularly annoyed certain persons, who might have been compromised by his speaking; but a most extraordinary event freed them from their embarrassment. The peace-officer and the two agents who arrested the culprit were leading him before the magistrate, when he cut his throat with a razor in the passage. In consequence of this strange suicide the most absurd rumours, though more or less true, circulated from mouth to mouth in the capital. Everybody was incriminated, except, perhaps, the real culprits; but in this instance, as in many others, they passed unnoticed, for their position and power insured them immunity.

CHAPTER IV.

MATHEO AND THE DANSEUSE.

TOWARDS the close of 1820, M. Dabasse, my peace officer, sent for me, and said,—

"In a house situated in the Rue le Peletier, facing the new opera building, resides a lady with her two daughters, very pretty girls, about twenty years of age. A man goes to see them daily, and spends the evening with them. The prefect of police wishes to know who this individual is; but if he perceive that he is followed, or that any watch is kept upon him, you lose your situation. You understand?"

I confess that I was greatly embarrassed to follow a man I did not at all know, and follow him without his suspecting it in the slightest: to learn who he was, what he did, and where he lived, appeared to me very difficult, especially by night. But as it is a principle of mine that nothing is impossible in this world, and as I had no other means of livelihood but my pay, I courageously set to work.

On leaving M. Dabasse, I proceeded to the Rue le

Peletier, to reconnoitre the approaches. It was a handsome house, of aristocratic appearance, and I went up to the porter, who was a shoe-maker by trade. After bowing to him civilly, I said,

"I should like to speak with you privately, sir. Could you grant me a few moments' attention?"

The Cerberus raised his spectacles, looked at me for a moment, and after this examination, which, though rapid, was not the less complete, he said, in a marked northern accent, "Very good: we will go out."

As may be seen, this functionary was anything but polite; but I knew the best way of taming him, and so soon as we were in the street I said to him, "What I have to impart to you is of so important a nature that I cannot possibly mention it here, where people are constantly passing. If you will kindly accept a glass of wine at my expense, we shall be far more comfortable than we can be here."

"Well, go on, then, I will follow you directly," and he returned to his lodge to doff his apron.

When we were seated face to face, and a bottle of Bordeaux had been uncorked, with a second in perspective, I began as follows:

"I fancied I noticed that you came from the North, for you have a Flemish accent."

"Yes, I come from St. Omer."

"Well, that is surprising," I answered; "why, we

are townsmen;" and in proof I mentioned a number of persons at St. Omer whom I knew very well, and while talking I made him drink. I humbly confess that I had no difficulty in inducing him to do so, for he was only too anxious to empty his glass. When we had disposed of three bottles (I might almost say when he had), I fancied that his speech was growing somewhat thick, and that the favourable moment had arrived to turn the conversation upon the lady with the daughters; so, pretending to tell him a secret, I said, "My master, the Marquis de Grandmaison, who is young and immensely rich, met about a month back on the Boulevard a lady, accompanied by two other young ladies, who reside on your third floor. Inflammable like all young men, he fell madly in love with the youngest. He immediately followed her, and thus discovered where the mother lived. At first, reason taking the upper hand, urged him to abandon the adventure; but love at length reassuming its rights, robbed him of all the repose that he previously enjoyed. I, therefore, resolved to come to you and learn who these ladies are. Be assured, that if you consent to further my master's desires, you will be magnificently rewarded, for his generosity surpasses even his love."

The good man admirably gorged the bait, and answered me with a cunning look,

"I am most ready to oblige your master, and to

prove it to you I will tell you all I know, which will not take long. The mamma, who goes by the name of Madame de St. Amour, calls herself the widow of a general officer; but to tell you the truth, I do not believe a word of it. I fancy that mother and daughters are simply adventuresses. They know nobody in the house, and are only visited by one gentleman, who, I think, is their providence. He comes every night at ten o'clock, and goes away at one in the morning."

"Who is the gentleman?"

"Oh, I do not know that. I am not aware either of his name or his rank; but one thing I do know, that I am beginning to grow tired of him. This has been going on for the last six months, and you will hardly believe, that though I am obliged to sit up for him every night, I have not yet seen the colour of his money."

"Well, the Marquis will be delighted to hear all these details, and will not forget you. But of which of the girls do you fancy him the lover?"

Having heard me say that my pretended master adored the younger, the old porter answered with imperturbable coolness,

"The elder, I am certain of it."

"No matter," I added, "it would be as well to know who this person is."

"Certainly; but how will you manage it."

"Well, I can only see one way. To-night I will take up my post on the Opera steps, and wait till our man comes out. When he is coming down stairs, you will step out of your lodge, accompany him to the street gate, and point him out to me by raising your cap. The rest is my business." Then, consulting my watch, I added, "It is late, and I must leave you. I shall hasten to communicate this good news to my master."

At the first stroke of midnight, I was installed on the Opera steps, waiting for the mysterious visitor to come out and accompany him home. At a quarter past one I saw the porter appear in the gateway with a well-dressed gentleman, and give the agreed on signal. My stranger proceeded toward the Boulevard and turned to the left in the direction of the St. Denis gate. As it was freezing awfully hard, he began running at full speed. I followed him; but he no sooner heard the noise which my boots made on the ground than he stopped short to see whether he were followed. We were almost facing the Rue de Sentier; without a moment's hesitation I turned into this street and concealed myself in a gateway; then hearing him start again, I took off my boots, and holding them in my hand, followed him again. He led me as far as the Porte St. Martin, knocked at the house next the theatre, and disappeared after closing the door behind him.

I knew where he slept, but I had yet to learn his name. This was the most difficult job of all; for if I made inquiries at such an hour of the porter, the latter would not fail to tell his lodger of the fact in the morning. Moments were precious, and hence putting on my boots again, I formed a daring plan. Breaking the ice in a gutter, I dipped in my pocket-book, and then rapped in my turn at the door. It opened, and to my delight the porter was still up.

"I have just found this," I said, as I offered him the dripping pocket-book, "in the gutter in front of your house. I fancy that I saw a gentleman enter a moment before, and it may belong to him."

While saying this, I felt in the pockets of my pretended find, as if seeking some clue to its owner, and casually asked the name of the gentleman who had just come in. The porter told me that it was M. Mathieu, a gentleman of fortune, who did not reside in the house, but frequently came to spend the night with an actress of the Porte St. Martin Theatre, whom he kept in great splendour, and whose beauteous form all Paris flocked at that time to see in the "Chaste Susannah." I knew all I wanted, and so I said—

"I am very sorry at having disturbed you unnecessarily; but I have just noticed a letter addressed to the owner of this pocket-book—M. David, No. 27, Boulevard Poissonière—and I will deliver it to him to-morrow morning. Good night, sir."

I gave my peace-officer a report of my proceedings. He congratulated me, and transmitted it verbatim to the Prefect. Two days after, M. Anglis sent to compliment me through M. Foudras, the Inspector-General. This was my first police adventure, and I shall remember it all my life; for I caught chilblains, which still cause me horrible suffering every year.

A short time after my nocturnal excursion, Mathieu, cashier of the Treasury, took to flight, leaving behind him a deficit of 1,800,000 francs. Owing to this disappearance, I was present at a search which the police thought it necessary to make in the apartments of Mademoiselle B., of the Porte St. Martin Theatre, in the hope of finding something there that would set them on the track of the fugitive; but unluckily we did not find what we sought.

Twenty years later, two French police agents were sent to Carlsruhe to fetch the ex-cashier Mathieu, who was in prison there for forgery, in order that he might undergo his sentence of fifteen years penal servitude.

CHAPTER V.

LACENAIRE—FRANÇOIS—AVRIL.

I WILL now make a long gap in my recollections: not that I was idle during the time; but throughout the reign of Charles X., and the early part of Louis Philippe's reign, I was engaged in political affairs, which are rather matters of history than my own experiences. I could, were it necessary, describe all the intrigues connected with the barricades of July, and the affair of the burial of General Lamarque, which has afforded Victor Hugo such a brilliant episode for his last and greatest work, "Les Misérables;" but I will pass on to matters which are more intimately connected with my duties as police agent.

On December 14th, 1834, a horrible crime cast horror and terror over the inhabitants of one of the most populous quarters of the capital. An old woman, the widow Chardon, living with her son in the Passage du Cheval Rouge, in the Rue St. Martin, was found assassinated in her lodgings; and the same hand that struck the mother had struck the son. Their lodgings were composed of two rooms, with a window in each:

one looking over the entrance of the passage into the Rue St. Martin; the other into the passage itself. In the first room, the son was lying in a pool of blood; a blood-stained axe, thrown down near him, and the way in which his skull was fractured, sufficiently indicated how the crime had been committed. In the second room, the mother's corpse was found lying on a bed: it was covered with pillows, sheets, and blankets, as if the murderer had wished to shun the sight. The broken furniture, the forced locks, and the scattered linen, moreover, afforded abundant testimony that robbery had been the motive of the assassination, and that both had been consummated.

Chardon the son, generally known as "the Aunt," was notorious for his abominable habits; and the public accusation fell at first, and naturally, upon the abject beings to whom he belonged. Among these unclean men several were arrested, but released for want of evidence; while others were simply watched, although this surveillance produced no better results. The police were beginning to relax their search, when a fresh attempt, quite as alarming as the one which I have just described, caused new fears among the population and attracted the attention of the authorities.

On December 20th, an individual, who seemed anxious to leave Paris within a few hours, called on Messrs. Maigre et Mallet, bankers, and requested them to present two bills of exchange, one of which was payable at the end of the month, at the residence of M. Mahossier, No. 66, Rue Montorgueil. On December 31st, one Genevey, a lad of eighteen, collecting clerk to the firm, proceeded, at half-past three P.M., to the house indicated on the bill, and found, on the fourth floor back a door on which the name Mahossier was written in large letters in chalk. He tapped, and found two men, apparently waiting for him, in a room, the only furniture in which consisted of two trusses of straw and a basket covered by a plank. The clerk had no sooner entered than the door was shut after him. One of the strangers tried to seize his portfolio, containing 10,000 francs in bank notes, and his bag containing 1100 francs in specie, while dealing him at the same time a violent blow on his right shoulder with a sharp triangular instrument, which penetrated to his chest; and the other stranger tried to stifle the victim's cries by forcibly pressing his hands on his mouth. But Genevey was strong; he resisted, in spite of his wound, and began shouting so loudly that the two assassins, afraid of being caught in the act, took to flight, left the house, and began running down the street, themselves crying "Stop thief!" as if in pursuit of a criminal.

Such was the information transmitted to the prefecture, upon which the detectives began to act, though unsuccessfully. It was not till ten days after that that they resolved to intrust to me the search after the two assassins, whom they declared it was impossible to find.

I determined, as my first step, to go and see the landlord of the house in the Rue Montorgueil, and asked him for an exact description of the two assassins, as the first ray of light to be thrown on the affair. As Mahossier had called on him several times, he described him to me without difficulty, but he had only seen his companion once, and then very imperfectly. Supplied with a description of the former, I attentively examined the name of Mahossier, written in white chalk on the door of the room in which the crime was committed, and I then visited the houses in which malefactors usually lodged. I examined several in vain, but, on reaching No. 107, Rue Faubourg du Temple, I remarked in M. Pageot's police-book, the name of Mahossier, and immediately beneath it, that of Ficellier, who had both come and left again on the same day. I questioned the landlord and his wife, and learned that the two individuals in question had occupied one room, and soon acquired a certainty that they were the men whom I wanted. The landlady, in reply to my questions, described Ficellier to me, and at each word she uttered, at each new trait she added in order to give resemblance to the portrait, my surprise increased. I felt certain that the description exactly corresponded with that of a certain François, who had been arrested some days previously for obtaining three barrels of wine by fraud. Full of this idea, I returned to the prefecture, and as François was still at the depôt, I went to his cell, and, taking my portfolio from my pocket, I opened it, pretending to be looking for a name which I had forgotten. "Ah," I said to him, "I have been racking my brains since yesterday to discover what motive induced you to lodge at Pageot's under the name of Ficellier; and I understand it still less, because you told me that you were innocent of the charge brought against you."

"Hang it," he answered me, "although I am not guilty, I knew that you had a warrant against me, and knowing the old adage, 'if I were accused of stealing the towers of Notre Dame, I should bolt,' I was not such a fool as to give my name, so that your agents might arrest me."

There was no longer a doubt; it was really François, who, under the name of Ficellier, had lodged in the Rue Faubourg du Temple with Mahossier, and, starting from this point, it must be he who played the part of accomplice in the affair of the Rue Montorgueil. I therefore made a report, in which I charged François with being one of the actors in the crime of December 31st.

The next day I returned to the Faubourg du Temple; Pageot was out, and I took advantage of the fact to make his wife talk, who was much less reserved than her husband on the matter of robbers. She confessed to me that the man who had lodged with her under the name of Mahossier, had previously done so under that of Baton. It was Baton, then, that I must seek, and being sure that I had one of the assassins under lock, I felt on the eve of seizing the second.

There was at that period, in the Rue de Bondy, almost facing the Château d'Eau, an establishment known by the name of the "Estaminet des Quatre Billards," which was frequented by nearly all the worst characters in Paris. I made inquiries of the landlord, and learned from him that Baton came every evening to play at billiards, but had not made his appearance yet. I saw at a glance that it was impossible for me to wait for him there; for the scoundrels who used the house, knowing me and my two agents perfectly well, did not take their eyes off us, and some of them had even bolted already. I went away, after informing the landlord that I would wait at a wine-shop at the corner of the Boulevard du Temple, until he let me know that Baton had arrived; but, reflecting that this man might easily betray me, and I had no certainty that he might not let the man I wanted escape, I placed one of my agents on the watch, who could see at a distance all who entered or left the café, without being seen himself. About nine in the evening, the agent came to us.

"Baton has just entered the café," he said to me.

"Are you certain?"

"Quite. A moment ago I saw two young men stop in front of the house. Then they came toward me, conversing, and one said to the other as they parted, 'Good night, Baton!' Then the latter entered the Quatre Billards."

"Forward, gentlemen!"

And followed by my two inspectors, I went toward the estaminet. I had scarce entered ere the landlord, not letting me speak, said to me,

"You have arrived just as I was going to send for you. That is Baton talking near the last billiard table with that tall young man in the pointed hat."

Baton was at once arrested, and went with us toward the prefecture. As we walked along, contradictory thoughts assailed my mind. According to Madame Pageot's revelation, there was no doubt but that the man whom I held was the one who had lodged in the Faubourg du Temple, under the name of Mahossier—and consequently, the assailant of Genevey; but I found no resemblance between this man and the description given by the victim and the landlord of the house in the Rue Montorgueïl. Baton, confronted with these two persons, was not recognised by either; but the landlord had not recognised François either when I brought him into his presence. I was therefore forced to set my prisoner at liberty; but we had learned from a convict in La Force, that Baton was intimately acquainted with a man of the name of Gaillard, his old comrade at Poissy prison. I met Baton as he left the depôt, and while pretending to be going home, I accompanied him as far as the Place de la Bastille. On the road the conversation turned, as if accidentally, upon Gaillard; then, equally accidentally, I led him to give me a description of him, which was identical with that of Mahossier, as drawn both by Genevey and Gousseaux. There was no longer a doubt left in my mind. The assailant of Genevey was no other than Gaillard, who, concealing his identity under the name of Mahossier, had gone to lodge at the house where he had already found shelter from the police by adopting the name of his companion Baton.

Only one thing was now left to be done,—find Gaillard and arrest him. I began by looking for his name in the various lodging-house lists; but here arose another difficulty: during the past year upwards of twenty Gaillards were entered in the police lists of the various lodging-houses, and I did not even know the Christian name of the man I wanted. On the second day, I came to a lodging-house in the Rue Marivaux, where I found a Gaillard inserted; and I asked the landlady if this individual received any visitors, and what sort of company he kept.

"Well, sir," she answered, "I never saw anybody come to him, except a woman with a handkerchief round her head, who indeed came very often; but I do not know her name or where she lives."

"And when he went away, did he leave nothing behind?—did he not forget some linen or papers?"

"Oh yes, I found a packet of republican songs."

"Did you keep them?"

"Yes, sir; here they are."

I hoped to find on the margin of these songs some remark which might throw light on my researches, and it was a lucky idea; for, among the papers, I found an insulting letter addressed to the prefect of police. While reading the letter, I was struck by the similitude existing between the characters and those forming the name of Mahossier on the door of the Rue Montorgueil.

The two writings were laid before experts, who positively declared that the same hand had written them both. From that moment the search after Gaillard received official sanction; and the name of Mahossier was laid aside as one which had been used to throw the police off the scent; and it was at this moment that an informer made a fruitless attempt to discover the assassin.

A man of the name of Avril, who was imprisoned in La Force for a year told the detectives that, if he were set at liberty for a week, he would pledge himself to find Gaillard, with whom he was intimately acquainted, if he had not left Paris. His services were accepted; and for some days Avril led me, as well as two agents, to various houses in which he supposed that Gaillard might be lodging under an assumed name. These researches leading to no result, Avril took us to a number of wine houses outside the gates, where he hoped to find the man whom we were seeking. But the culprit was not fated to fall into our hands yet, and Avril went back to La Force.

On January 9th, as I said, I had denounced François as an accomplice of Mahossier, or rather of Gaillard, because he had lived with the latter under the name of Ficellier, at Pageot's. In consequence of this report, the head of the detective department told me to fetch François from Sainte-Pelagie to his office, in order to draw from him, if it were possible, some information as to the attempt in the Rue Montorgueil. I fetched the prisoner; and as we rolled along in the fiacre, we talked about one thing or other, till François suddenly said,

"M. Canler, I not only know the assassins of Mother

Chardon and her son, but all the circumstances of the affair. I am the more certain of this, because I heard them from one of the murderers. This is how I did so.

"On January 1st, as I was walking across the Place Royale, I found myself face to face with Gaillard and a stranger, who I afterwards learned, was a man of the name of H——, a pocket-book maker. We wished one another a happy new-year. For a while, we talked about the weather, and then, as Gaillard invited me to breakfast, we proceeded to a wine shop, and were soon comfortably installed. We breakfasted rather slowly, for, at one o'clock the next morning, Gaillard and myself were still seated opposite each other. H—— had left at an early hour; one bottle succeeded the other, our heads had grown hot, and the hour for confidence had arrived. 'Listen to me,' Gaillard said; 'I and H—— murdered Mother Chardon and her son, and this is how matters occurred. I went with H—— to the Passage du Cheval Rouge, and, leaving him on the watch, I went up to Chardon whom I had known for a long time. I found him in the front room, and immediately, without giving him time to look round, I leapt upon him, and his account was settled. As for his mother, she was in the second room, and I soon finished her off too. This double job completed, I began searching, pocketed a few wretched twenty and forty franc pieces, and then went down; but when I reached the street I found H—— paler than a ghost, with haggard eyes, and scarce able to stand. 'You are a coward, and a poltroon,' I said to him, 'with you a man would go straight to the guillotine!' The truth was, that with his frightened looks, he was capable of having me arrested in the act.' "Such," François continued, "were the terms in which Gaillard described to me the affair in the Cheval Rouge Passage."

So soon as I reached the prefecture, I reported the statement François had made to me, which he repeated to the magistrate. After this revelation, Gaillard, who was only inculpated in the attempted assassination in the Rue Montorgueil, was the principal culprit in the double murder.

Soon after, an apparently futile piece of information led us to discover that Gaillard was not the assassin's real name. Avril, the prisoner in la Force, whom I had walked about uselessly for a week, stated that Gaillard had an aged aunt who lived in the Rue Bar-du-Bec. The chief of the detectives and myself proceeded to the house indicated, and after going up to the second floor, rang a bell by a door, in the centre of which was a paled trap. No one answered the first ring, so I rang a second time; the trap opened, and a cracked voice asked, "what do you want?"

"To speak to Madame Gaillard."

"I am the person."

"We wish, madame, to speak to you about your nephew Gaillard."

"In the first place, gentlemen, my nephew's name is Lacenaire, and not Gaillard; in the next, he is a bad fellow, and I am greatly afraid of being assassinated by him; that is why I have had the trap made in my door, that I may see the persons who ring, and if he were to come I should be very careful not to open to him."

Hence, according to this information, the human chameleon, who first called himself Mahossier and then Gaillard, assumed a fresh name, that of Lacenaire, though this was not his last; for, a few days later, we received information from Beaune that Lacenaire had been arrested in that town under the name of Levy Jacob, at the moment when he was trying to pass a forged note.

Can we comprehend after this how a man, who so frequently changed his name, and who seemed so anxious to conceal his identity, could have lodged at Pageot's under that of Mahossier, which he had employed to trap his victim?

Lacenaire was at once sent to Paris. On his arrival, M. Allard and myself went to see him in his cell, where he was lying in fetters upon a small camp bed. We spoke to him about the crime in the Rue

Montorgueil, and he confessed that he was one of the actors in it, without any effrontery or remorse. He spoke about it as a merchant would speak of an unsuccessful speculation. We then asked him who his accomplices were, but he answered vehemently, "Gentlemen, though we may be villains, we possess a self pride, which consists in never denouncing our accomplices, unless they have betrayed us; hence, you must not expect me to mention any one."

"I do not require you to speak," I replied, "for we know your accomplice; it is François," (Lacenaire smilingly denied) and I can tell you also that it was you who murdered Chardon and his mother."

Then I told him all that François had revealed. "Ah," he said, when I had finished. "François told you that, did he? very well, when I get to La Force I will inquire, and, afterwards we will see."

"Not only has François denounced you, but I went about with Avril for a week to try and discover you, Avril performing the part of denouncer at his own request."

"Ah, he too," Lacenaire continued, "really, he too. Well, gentlemen, I shall have the honour of seeing you again after a while."

In fact, some time after this interview, M. Allard and myself were informed that Lacenaire desired to speak with us. After he had been taken to La Force he was removed from that prison by the judges and was now in the "Mouse-trap," a large subterraneous hall, in which prisoners awaiting examination were kept. The keeper's wife, Mother André, introduced us. Lacenaire was alone. He bowed, and said :—

"Gentlemen, when you came to see me at the depot of the prefecture, you told me of what François had said about me, and what Avril had done to procure my arrest. I answered you, that I would inquire, and I have done so. I told you also, that villains of my stamp never denounce any but those who have betrayed them ; well, all that François told you with reference to the Chardon murder is true, except poor H—'s complicity ; for he knew nothing about it and is an honest man. I will tell you all the details of the double crime and my accomplices in it, as well as in the Rue Montorgueil affair. M. Canler was not deceived about the latter, and François was really my companion. I am well aware that I shall be condemned to penal servitude for life for it, while for the former crime I shall lay my head under the knife. But what would you have? It is the only way I have left by which to avenge myself on François and Avril, who betrayed me in such a cowardly fashion."

And then, with an indignation derived from rancour, Lacenaire told us the details of these two assassinations, which I will not repeat, as the trial made them so thoroughly known, but which incontestibly proved the complicity of François and Avril.

After his trial, and contrary to the usual custom with persons capitally condemned, Lacenaire, in consequence of his revelations, remained at the Conciergerie, where he wrote his Memoirs. He was confined in a cell at the end of the left-hand gallery, but as it was considered necessary to prevent him killing himself by strangulation or by opening an artery, in a moment of desperation or in order to avoid the disgrace of execution, a keeper never left him night or day. Whenever I had occasion to go to the Conciergerie, I never failed to pay him a visit, and when I entered his cell he at once rose, walked to meet me with a gracious look, bowed with a smile on his lips, offered me a chair, and asked in the most natural way, how I was; then the conversation nearly always turned on matters independent of his situation. One day, however, when I found him very busy with his Memoirs, I ventured to allude to the subject by saying:—

"Ah, ah! so you are working for posterity; it will be very curious."

"Will it not? 'The Memoirs of an Assassin!' It is rather out of the common track. I fancy the public will read my book eagerly for the sake of the novelty."

"And of the author," I added.

On hearing this remark, he bowed with a smile; a

slight blush suffused his cheeks, and I saw, as it were, a ray of personal satisfaction and internal contentment illumine his countenance. It was a wretched pride, compelled to seek its origin, cause, and motive in the frightful celebrity which his crimes had obtained for him.

Many serious and painful reflections did I make while listening to the remarks, often full of sense and wit, of this criminal, whose head was so soon to fall on the scaffold. The prejudices he nourished against society had not yet entirely perverted all other feelings in him; and most assuredly if he had not professed so great an aversion against humanity generally, and had not pride and envy so utterly ruled him, he was gifted with qualities sufficiently remarkable for him to have made his way honourably in the world.

On another day, I turned the conversation on the affair of the Rue Montorgueil.

"I think," I said to him, "that you proved utterly false to your usual habits of prudence in that matter."

"What do you mean?"

"Had you succeeded in assassinating Genevey, you would have fled, taking with you his money and notes; but the corpse must necessarily have remained in the room. And the only difference between what has happened and what would have happened in the other event is, that a dead man would have been found instead of a dying one. Once the police were warned, we should have equally sought you, and I should have discovered, as I did, that Mahossier was no other than Baton, next Gaillard, and, lastly, Lacenaire, and you would have fallen into our hands just the same."

"Pray make no mistake, sir. When I undertook any affair of that sort, I always carefully foresaw the result, and prevented consequences. Straw was found in the room: well, if Genevey had fallen, I should have cut his body to pieces, and then put it in a chest with that straw which I had brought expressly. This job finished, I should have hired, a few leagues from Paris, a small villa with a garden. And then water boiling for twenty hours would have completely decomposed the body, and fire would have completed the work of destruction by reducing the whole to ashes, which I should have buried. You can see that I should then have been able to defy all the police in the world and yourself to discover the slightest proof of the crime. Besides, everybody would have known of the disappearance of the clerk without suspecting the cause. And you would have been the first to think, with many others, that he had bolted in order to appropriate the sum which he had about him. Since you have told me, Monsieur Canler, of the steps you took to discover me, I have seen that I acted very wrong in having any accomplice in the affair of the Rue Montorgueil as well as the other. I could have done the job alone, and certainly have done it better, for I should not have missed Genevey, who only owes his life to the poltroonery of François, who fled at the young man's first cries. I should then have had some 12,000 francs, on which I could have lived comfortably for three or four years, and thus foiled all pursuit. On the other hand, if I had not had François for accomplice, he could not have made any revelations to you. If Avril had not shared with me in the murder of widow Chardon and her son, I should not have required to confess that double murder and lay down my life for the sake of destroying the man who betrayed me. I am obliged to confess," he added, with a laugh, "that in those two instances I acted like a raw recruit. And it was the more foolish on my part, because I ought to have remembered that I had managed very well alone on prior occasions."

"How so?"

"Oh! they are past affairs and quite forgotten."

"Perhaps you think so!"

"I am certain of it! Still, I was alone in those matters, and can tell you about them, as they compromise nobody, and will prove to you that when a man has his free will, he has always greater liberty of action, or of stopping betimes. When I was at Lyons, then, I went one night to Brotteaux's, to have an orgie with some companions, whom I left at about two in the morning. I was returning to my lodgings alone, when, on crossing the Moraud bridge, I met a very well-dressed gentleman, on whose waistcoat a heavy chain glittered. His walk was rather tottering: I went up to him; we were alone on the bridge, and, as I heard no sound, with one hand I clutched his throat, and with the other took his watch and chain, as well as his portfolio, which was in a side coat-pocket, and, by-the-bye, contained five one thousand franc notes: then, taking advantage of his unconscious state, I caught him up and threw him into the Rhone, where he disappeared. I never knew who the man was, and indeed did not bother about him, as I had worked alone, and hence had nothing to fear.

"Another time, shortly after I was discharged from Poissy prison, I came to live at Paris; and as I possessed a small sum of money, I went to the Palais Royal to try my fortune in a gambling-house, and in a few minutes was cleaned out. By my side was a young man whom chance favoured in a most peculiar manner, for whenever he backed either red or black he won, and hence, at ten in the evening, he went off with a dozen thousand-franc notes. On seeing him leave, the idea suddenly occurred to me of following him, killing him, and then seizing his notes. But I reflected that it was too early for me to hope to carry out my plan with success. I said to myself, 'A game deferred is not lost.' The next night and the following nights I was at the green table, waiting for a new fortune's favourite, who would give me a prospect of success by leaving at midnight. It was my eighth night of waiting, when I saw, about midnight, a gentleman arrive, who stood opposite to me. He staked a five hundred franc note on red: he won, and went on winning, so that at one o'clock in the morning he placed in his pocket-book 30,000 francs in notes, and went off. I followed him, and on reaching a dark part of the Rue Blanche, I went up to the lucky gambler, and, raising a dagger, I threatened to stab him if he uttered a single word. The poor devil did not speak, for he was more dead than alive, and I was about to seize, without any difficulty, the object of my desire, when we heard the measured tread of a patrol coming towards us. His courage at once returned, and he began crying with all his might, 'Help! murder!' I had only just time to run off at full speed and escape the clutches of the patrol. I was alone and luckily escaped; but if I had had a comrade, I should have felt anxious about him. He would have been in my way, and in all probability one of us would have lost his liberty for a moment of clumsiness. The ill success of this affair caused me to reflect, and I gave up this mode, which I at first thought infallible, but which offered too great danger in carrying out."

I had listened, without interruption, to this coldly criminal being; but at last I summoned up my thoughts and said,

"Do you know, Lacenaire, it is fortunate for humanity that there are but few men in society like yourself?"

"You mean," he replied, "that the society against which I declared war, and which I have so long pursued with an implacable hatred, will be glad to see my head roll? I know it! it has conquered me, and it is but fair that I should undergo the law of retaliation."

Another day I invited him to make revelations about crimes which he might have committed with accomplices, or any, the details of which had reached his knowledge.

"You would thus render," I said to him, "a great service to society, which would certainly feel grateful to you."

"And why do you wish me to try and deserve the gratitude of society? Have I not been its cruel enemy? Have I not waged obstinate war upon it, and have I not pursued it with all the means in my power? No, no! if I ever were to make revelations, it would be for the sake of being useful to the police, who have treated me very kindly, for which I am infinitely obliged to them. And then, again, why should I do so? Would it in any way alter my position? No; and moreover, I prefer taking with me to the tomb the esteem of those wretched beings whom want, suffering, and the ingratitude of society have forced upon the path which I myself followed."

I answered, that the motives which he offered in excuse of crime could not be accepted; that it was acknowledged that vices alone engendered the guilty, who then demanded resources from crime rather than labour, by which to secure a comfort of which they were unworthy, or to satisfy their passions.

"I will not argue with you," he answered; "but do not expect, for all that, to draw anything from me. I have told you my opinion about denouncing, and I shall not depart from it."

Lacenaire and Avril were condemned to death, and their heads were about to fall in a few days. By one of those emotions which it is impossible to define, these two men, who had hated each other so as to ensure their mutual destruction, were now sincerely reconciled, and they were allowed to dine together in order to celebrate this reconciliation. Among other courses was a roast fowl, and Avril, while cutting off the legs, noticed some blood on his knife, and exclaimed, "Hilloh! it is not done enough; look at the blood, Lacenaire."

"Well," Lacenaire answered, "I don't suppose that you are frightened of blood."

And they began joking about the blood they had shed, and their own which was soon about to flow. Frightful facts, which proved the cold cruelty of these two wretches!

On January 9, 1836, they were removed to Bicêtre prison. They perfectly understood the motive, and said, "Ah, ah, I see that it will soon be over." In fact, on that same evening I got into a fiacre with the chief of the detectives and my secretary. We had to inform the condemned that their execution was fixed for the morrow, but that, if they had any revelations to make, a respite would be granted. This was attacking a man in his last intrenchments, and flashing in his eyes the image of an indefinite prolongation of a life whose term was fixed.

Avril was brought to the office. The chief told him the object of our visit; and Avril, with his usual coolness, confined himself to saying, "I have no remark to make." Lacenaire was brought in his turn. He came in, us usual, with a smile on his lips, and saying,—

"Good evening, gentlemen; how are you?"

"Lacenaire," M. Allard said to him, "I am ordered by the prefect of police to ask you whether you have any revelations to make."

But while uttering these words, M. Allard turned frightfully pale, and he stammered rather than uttered them, which, under the circumstances, was almost equivalent to a sentence of death.

"Ah, it is only that!" Lacenaire, who noticed him tremble, interrupted him; "reassure yourself, sir! I believe that you have come to inform me that it is for to-morrow? Well, as soon to-morrow as later, as it must come to that in the end. I shall be over with my troubles all the sooner."

Then, after exchanging a few careless remarks with us, he said, as he was leaving, "By-the-bye, gentlemen, I trust that I shall have the honour of seeing you to-morrow morning at the Barrière St. Jacques?"

We nodded, and he was taken back to his cell. A few minutes after, as we crossed the courtyard to reach our vehicle, a well-known voice smote on our ear. It was that of Lacenaire, who occupied a cell next to Avril, and was now conversing with his accomplice.

"By the way, Avril," he said, "I forgot to mention something to M. Allard; shall I send for him?"

On hearing this, we stopped to listen.

"Well," the other replied, "send for him, he can't be far."

"Ah, stuff! it's not worth while."

Then, a moment later, he said to his accomplice in a loud voice,—

"Avril, the ground will be very cold to-morrow!"

"That's true," the other answered.

And a moment of silence followed these remarks.

"Father Thomas," Avril continued, addressing the keeper ordered to watch him through the night, "I cause you a deal of bother, don't I, old boy?"

"Well, it's my trade, my lad."

The conversation went no further; for Lacenaire, again addressing his accomplice, cried to him, "Good night, Avril, good night."

"Good night, Lacenaire," the other answered.

We went away, greatly affected at having heard this dialogue between two men who, ten hours later, were going to die by the hand of the executioner. On the next morning, the vehicle that conveyed them did not reach the scaffold till a quarter to nine, owing to the wretched state of the roads. These are the words in which the *Gazette des Tribunaux* described this double expiation:—

"At a quarter to nine the mournful procession reached the foot of the scaffold, which had been erected an hour after midnight by torchlight. Lacenaire hurriedly descended from the vehicle, the pallor of his face was frightful, his glance vague and uncertain, he stammered and seemed searching for words, which his tongue refused to articulate. Avril got out after him, with a quick, decided step, and took a tranquil glance at the public; perfectly resigned, he walked up to Lacenaire and embraced him.

"'Good bye, old fellow,' he said; 'I am going to open the ball.' He firmly ascended the scaffold steps, he was fastened to the fatal plank, and then turned round and said, 'Come, Lacenaire, old fellow, be courageous, and imitate me.' It was his last remark, and the knife sent his head rolling on the planks of the scaffold. During this horrible moment, Lacenaire was standing at the foot of the scaffold, and the Abbé Montes sought to distract his attention from the frightful sight which he had before him. 'Oh, stuff!' Lacenaire replied, in a shaking voice; but in vain did he try to produce a belief in an assurance which he did not possess. 'Is Monsieur Allard there?' he asked, in a still fainter voice. 'Yes,' replied M. Canler, assistant-chief of the detective department. 'Ah!—I—am—very—glad of it.' He had announced that he intended to address the people, but he had not the strength left; his legs gave way; his face was changed; he ascended the steps, supported by the executioner's assistants, and the fatal stroke soon put an end to his anguish and his life."

In the report of the *Gazette des Tribunaux*, all that relates to Avril is strictly correct, but what is said about Lacenaire is not exactly so. I saw all that took place. I heard all that was said at the execution, for I was close to the scaffold and the sufferers, to whom I spoke, and the whole of this gloomy episode has remained graven on my memory in an ineffaceable way. The following is the exact narrative :—

Lacenaire actively descended from the coach, embraced Avril, and, noticing me on his right hand, he bowed painfully, and said, "There you are! good morning, Monsieur Canler: it is very kind of you to have come: is M. Allard here?" I replied in the affirmative. During this colloquy his face was smiling and did not evince the slightest anxiety. Avril boldly ascended the scaffold steps, and when he was fastened to the fatal planks, he threw his head back and cried, in a powerful voice, "Good bye, my old Lacenaire! courage!" To which Lacenaire replied energetically, "Good bye, good bye!" Demarest, the executioner of Beauvais, who had come to help in this double execution, then went up to Lacenaire, and, taking him by the shoulders, forced him to turn, so that he should not see the instrument of punishment. Lacenaire yielded to the impulse, but turning again directly, he raised his head to contemplate the frightful scene that was taking place behind him; he contemplated the knife suspended over the head of his accomplice, and looked at it twice, defiantly saying, "I am not afraid, no, I am not afraid," and it was only by main force that he could be made to turn away. Ere long, he himself mounted the steps calmly, and a moment after ceased to exist.

In order to do homage to the truth, I must here explain the contradiction between the newspaper report and my narrative. The eccentric manner in which Lacenaire had behaved when under examination at the trial, had gained him a deplorable celebrity, owing to the persistency with which the daily press attracted the curiosity of readers to this great criminal. The remarks reported, the publication of the verses he composed, the announcement of the speedy issue of his memoirs, might prove a very contagious example for certain characters inclined to believe themselves misunderstood by society, and pursued by the fatal desire of attaining celebrity, no matter of what nature. This consideration determined the authorities on trying to show, on behalf of morality, that Lacenaire, the great criminal, the great assassin, the man who made a sport of the life of his fellow-men, and had shed their blood with cold cruelty, broke down in his last moments, and did not "die game."

The *Gazette des Tribunaux* had entrusted to a literary gentleman, not connected with the staff, the duty of reporting the execution; but as he was unable to approach the scaffold, he obtained his information from the prefecture, which was given him in the desired sense.

Such are the facts which I thought I ought not to refrain from recording; because, in telling my recollections, I resolved to be truthful, and the motives which induced the authorities to alter the truth no longer exist. Twenty-five years have elapsed since this sinister affair, and since speculation seized on the sayings and doings of this criminal to supply them to the greedy curiosity of the public, without inquiring whether it were not erecting a pedestal for crime thus to record the acts and words of a villain with that minute care which should only be employed when the object is to restore the honour of an innocent victim to a fatal error.

CHAPTER VI.

AN ELOPEMENT.

A RICH landed gentleman, residing in one of the departments adjoining Paris, informed the prefect of police that his wife, a young and charming brunette of three-and-twenty, had eloped with a M. V——, her seducer, carrying off to the value of 150,000 francs in money and jewellery.

I was ordered to set out in pursuit of the fugitives, with no other instructions than "seek, and you will find." I went straight to the post-house, where I learned, to my great satisfaction, that on the previous evening a lady and gentleman had ordered horses for ten o'clock the same night, that the chaise in which they travelled was their own, that the body was painted green, and that they had expressed an intimation of proceeding to England. Provided with this information and the description given me, I returned to the prefecture to announce my discovery, and two hours later I left the capital in an excellent post-chaise as fast as the horses could drag me. I had a passport for England, and a warrant to arrest the truant pair, and at each change of horses I picked up the trail of the lovers. Nothing could be more simple than the system I employed. When I reached a station, and while the horses were being changed, I carefully asked the post-boys and ostlers for a description of the travellers who had passed since the previous evening, and constantly backing up my request with an irresistible argument in the shape of five-franc pieces, I thus picked up from post to post certain proofs of their having passed. I had not, so to speak, lost them out of sight, and by hurrying my post-boys, I was certain of catching them up before they em barked. But, at the chief town of the department of the Somme, I learned from an ostler that on this very morning a gentleman and a young lady, who arrived in a post-chaise, had started for Arras, after breakfasting and taking a little rest; but they had scarce left Amiens, when they told the postilion to turn back, and take the Metz road, as they wished, so they said, to visit Germany.

It was impossible for me to go further, as my passport was *viséed* for London. I thought that V——, by choosing another road, would fancy that he had completely thrown out any pursuers, would take his time in travelling, and thus enable me to catch him up. Consequently, jumping into my post-chaise, the horses of which had been changed, I went back to Paris, where I arrived during the night. At ten the next morning I started again, but this time with a passport for Germany.

At Chalons-sur-Marne, I found traces of them again: they had been seen, but they had not stopped. I followed them at full pelt, lavishing five-franc pieces on the post-boys, and thus obtaining the most exact information from mouth to mouth. At Metz, I learned that they had arrived on the previous evening, had gone to bed, and started again at nine o'clock that morning; but I also learned that, instead of proceeding to Germany, as they had expressed an intention, my travellers were *en route* for Switzerland. Time pressed, and I wanted to arrest them in France; hence I tripled the drink money of my post-boys, and the horses tripled their speed. I so soon regained lost time, that I caught up my fugitives at a little village a few paces from the frontier. It was high time. The post-house was the first building in the village, and imagine my delight when I noticed in the inn yard the green post-chaise which I had been following for such a length of time. I proceeded to the mayor, the sole authority whose intervention I should claim, and found him fork in hand, pitching straw into his out-house. This municipal magistrate was a stout, short man, with a jolly face, whose slightly copperas nose displayed a marked weakness for the gifts of Bacchus. To complete his portrait, add bare feet thrust into heavy wooden shoes, a patched blouse, and a blue cotton nightcap. I explained to him the object of my calling on him, and, after producing my authority, requested him to render me his assistance. Then a rather absurd scene took place. The worthy man, ashamed at receiving in such attire a "monsieur" who had come from Paris in a post-chaise, perfectly ignorant of the modest value of my title of chief police inspector, and perhaps fancying that he had to deal with some exalted functionary, began apologizing profusely, while assuring me that I could do perfectly well without him; and, in fact, that he did not at all understand what I wanted of him. After an infinity of explanations, I drove the fact into him that his presence was necessary to legalize my acts; and the good man, after begging me to wait for a minute, reappeared in his Sunday coat and official scarf, holding in one hand a roll of paper, in the other a pen and ink-bottle. We went towards the post-house, and meeting on our way a gendarme and his corporal, the mayor requested them to join us. On reaching the inn, I found the chaise still at the same spot, and my lovers were at breakfast. Their room was pointed out to us, and I proceeded there with the mayor and the two gendarmes.

"M. V—— ?" I asked, on entering.

"That is my name, sir," said the fugitive Don Juan.

"As you are a traveller, you must have papers, a passport, to prove your individuality."

V—— looked at me with a frown, but the young lady turned pale. Still, there was no chance of evading the question; and the presence of the two cocked-hats adorning either side of the door, gave irresistible force to my words. He yielded, and handed me his passport, which was quite in order.

"That is very well," I said, after glancing at it; "but the lady?"

"The lady is my wife," V—— answered, haughtily, "and requires no passport to travel with me."

"Are you sure of that?"

"Certainly, sir; and I do not understand——"

"What! Madame D—— does not require a passport to travel with M. V——?"

On hearing her name, the young lady uttered a cry and lost her senses. I then went up to her seducer, and, laying my hand on his shoulder, I said to him—

"In the name of the law, sir, you are my prisoner!"

V—— fell into a chair, and saw clearly that he had lost the game. I summoned the landlady; and while she was attending to Madame D——, under the paternal eye of the corporal of gendarmes, I went down into the yard with the Mayor, V——, and his aiguiletted keeper, to examine the post-chaise. As I entered the vehicle by one door, V—— dashed through the other, and tried to raise a cushion. I pushed him out, and found under the cushion a pair of pocket-pistols, thorough toys, but deadly toys, which he possibly intended to try upon me. We found in the chaise the jewels and the greater portion of the cash; the difference had been spent in purchasing the post-chaise and defraying the travelling expenses. When it came to drawing up a report of the arrest, it was a very different story. The Mayor, laying aside all false shame, told me that he had never done such a thing in his life, and had not the remotest idea how he was to set about it. I was obliged to dictate it to him; after which, leaving V—— in the hands of the two gendarmes, to be sent to Paris from post to post, I got into the post-chaise with Madame D——, and we set out for the capital, where I restored my pretty prisoner to the conjugal domicile. Then, the husband sent V—— two hundred and fifty francs, that he might travel post; and, on the seducer's arrival, M. D——, who wished to avoid any scandal, withdrew the charge, and challenged V——; but through a contrast which is rather frequent in the turpitude of the human heart, this Lovelace, who with women affected noble and generous sentiments in order to win their love, declined the challenge; and a few months after managed to send a letter to Madame D——, in which he urged her to poison her husband, and offered to provide her with the necessary means to accomplish this abominable crime!

Terrified by such monstrosity, the repentant wife threw herself at her husband's feet, and gave him the letter which she had just received Reassured as to her feelings, M. D—— frankly forgave her: as for the criminal proposition, of which he held the proof, he confined himself to informing the police of the letter and the accompanying circumstances; and, while preventing the evil as far as was possible, he refrained from having his name linked in the newspapers with that of a villain who was unworthy to be a member of society.

CHAPTER VII.

THE ASSASSINATION OF WIDOW HOULT.

THE Widow Houet, seventy years of age, and possessing a fortune of about 150,000 francs, lived, in 1821, at No. 81, Rue St. Jacques. She was the mother of two children, a boy and a girl. The daughter was married to a retired wine-merchant of the name of Robert, who did not always live on the best terms with his mother-in-law; as for the son, a tall, powerful fellow, with a weak, limited brain, he lived with his mother, and worked at a shop, where he earned two francs a day as odd-man.

The old lady, although rich considering her condition, had no servant except a charwoman, who came every morning to clean up and go of errands. On September 13th of this same year, 1821, the charwoman came later than usual, for which she scolded her rather severely, and then sent her on a long errand. After her departure, a strange person came to Widow Houet and took her away, no one knew whither, for she never returned.

Public opinion, based on the ill-terms subsisting between son and mother-in-law, publicly accused the former of this disappearance, by which he directly profited, as he became heir to one half of Madame Houet's fortune. Robert was consequently arrested, as well as one of his friends, of the name of Bastien, who was a jobbing carpenter. There was an inquiry, but as no proof was produced in support of the charge the prisoners were set at liberty.

Three years later, fresh evidence having been obtained, Robert and Bastien were again arrested, and subjected to a severe cross-examination, but were liberated by a judge's order. Nearly ten years had elapsed since the last arrest; a few months more and the decennial statute of limitations would throw its protecting cloak over the crime and leave it unpunished. Public rumour had been silent for a long time; the disappearance of Widow Houet was forgotten by many, and unknown by more, when in March, 1833, a man of the name of C——, a liberated convict and sort of man of business, who was a friend and adviser of Bastien, came to a fellow-convict, an ex-agent of Vidocq's brigade, now attached to the detective force as spy, and told him confidentially that if the police would give him five hundred francs, he would denounce the widow Houet's murderers, and supply sufficiently certain indications to find her corpse.

The proposition was laid before our chief, and, as may be supposed, at once accepted, and I was ordered to hear C——'s revelations. He began by telling me that Robert was the instigator of the crime, and that Bastien had only assented, upon repeated promises of money from the former—promises which he had not kept, for, as the civil tribunal only allotted Widow Houet's daughter an income of fifteen hundred francs a year until the expiration of the time decided by law for the inheritance of persons who had disappeared, Robert, owing to this hitch, which he had not foreseen, had first evaded his promises and then to some extent forgotten them, no longer remembering that the hand which his accomplice offered him was still dyed with the blood of their victim.

"Very lately," C—— continued, "Bastien confided to me that he expected Robert would give him this time what he had so long promised, for he had written to him at Villeneuve le Roi, whither he had retired with his wife, and the letter contained, among other menaces, these words:

"'*Remember the garden at No.* 81 *Rue Vaugirard, you know, fifteen feet from the end wall, and fourteen feet from the side wall. The dead may sometimes return!*'

"Bastien," C—— said, "has in his pocket-book a plan of this garden, on which the spot where Widow

Houet was buried is marked by a black cross. I have for a long time possessed Bastien's confidence, and more than once he has himself told me all the details of this assassination."

"Well," we said to him, "do you remember these with sufficient exactness to repeat them to us?"

"Oh, yes; and to be more certain, I will repeat word by word the last conversation which Bastien and I had on the subject.

"'Robert,' he said to me, 'had for a long time been telling me of his disputes with his mother-in-law, and the wrongs she had done him, and he reproached her, among other things, with being an old miser, who, though possessing a fortune, left her children in want. He many times repeated to me, that after the death of his wife's mother one half this fortune would come to him, and the conclusion of his remarks always was, 'The old hunks will never die to get us out of trouble.'

"'At length, in the beginning of September, 1821, he proposed to me to assassinate her, offering, if I assented, to share with me the inheritance which would accrue to him. I accepted the bargain.

"'Robert then took No. 81, Rue Vaugirard, a detached house with a garden, in which I dug a deep hole. I also bought a rope, and laid in a stock of quick-lime; after which I went one Sunday morning to the widow, and told her that her daughter and son-in-law expected her to breakfast at their new house. As the old woman had known me for a long while as a friend of her children, she had no suspicion; she was alone too, as the charwoman had gone out, and a few minutes after we were both seated in a fiacre, and proceeding in the direction of the Rue Vaugirard.

" 'While we were talking in the coach I drew from my pocket the rope which I intended for her, telling her that I had bought it for some purpose or the other, and we joked about its strength and size. We got out of the fiacre a few doors from No. 81, and I dismissed the driver, so that he might not know where we went. When we entered the garden, I threw the rope round the old woman's neck, and she was strangled in a second. I then tried to throw her into the hole which I had prepared, but as it was too narrow, I was obliged to put her in upright, and the body sinking together was thus seated on its heels. I at once covered the body with a thick coating of lime, and then carefully levelled the ground. This operation ended, I went to eat the breakfast prepared to serve, if necessary, as a bait for Widow Houet.

" 'That dog of a Robert, far from keeping the promises which he had made me, led me on from month to month, from year to year, giving me every now and then some paltry sums; and up to the present he has remained deaf to my friendly expostulations as well as to my threats; but I have just written him a letter, which I feel certain will produce its effect, and I shall receive money before long. It is high time, for in a few months I should be unable to do anything with him, as the ten years' limitation would free him from all fear, and give him the right of walking with his head erect.'

"And it is in this letter, gentlemen," C—— continued, "that the indications are to which I referred, and which describe so exactly the spot where the body of the unhappy woman may be found."

Two warrants were issued against the villains, and our chief with an inspector proceeded to Villeneuve-le-Roi in order to arrest Robert; but the latter, after a violent altercation which he had a few days previously with Bastien, who had come to ask for money, threatening to make revelations to justice if he did not receive it, had hurriedly started for Bourbonne, under the pretext of restoring his wife's health, but in reality to escape the presence of his accomplice. Our chief and his agent, therefore, went on to Bourbonne-les-Bains, and brought back the husband and wife.

On the day of their departure I was instructed to seize Bastien. Accompanied by two police agents, we set ourselves upon the watch at the corner of the Rue du Buisson St. Louis. At mid-day I saw a tall powerful man, aged about fifty, and dressed in a blue coat with brass buttons ; in a word, closely resembling the description of Bastien, turn the corner of the street. At once I ordered my agents to hold back till they saw me struggling with this individual, and then hasten to my assistance. Then, walking toward Bastien, I passed without looking at him, lest I should arouse his attention ; but I had scarce got beyond him ere I turned, and holding him very tightly with my arms, rendered it impossible for him to use his own.

"Help !" I shouted to my men.

"Thieves !" Bastien yelled, as he gave me plenty of kicks and struggled furiously. But I held on. My agents came up, and each held an arm, while I felt in my gentleman's coat pocket. I took his portfolio without resistance, and we then proceeded to his lodgings to wait till the police commissary, for whom I at once sent, arrived, to make a search.

We found in the pocket-book :—1. The plan of the garden at No. 81, Rue Vaugirard, and the mark showing the spot where the corpse was buried. 2. Two notes referring to this affair, on the back of one of which was a copy of the plan, with the words, "I send you the plan of your old garden in the Rue Vaugirard, in which you made such progress in 1821."

Lastly, among the papers we discovered several notes relating to the inheritance of Widow Houet, and another in C——'s handwriting, specifying that according to a verdict of 1825, it was not possible to prosecute Robert at present, but that Bastien could no longer longer be troubled, even if he were to confess or were found guilty. Bastien and Robert were locked up at the prefecture a few days after one another.

The next point was to prove the existence of the proof of the crime, and we feared lest, while waiting for the judicial inquiry, the accomplices of the prisoners, if they had any, might try to get rid of the corpse and thus destroy the evidence. In order to prevent this, I was told to establish a watch in the house where the crime had been committed. My instructions were to guard against any alteration in the present state of things being made, but it was most important that the occupiers or lodgers in the house should not learn the object of the surveillance.

I humbly confess that on leaving the prefecture with the two agents whom I had selected for this duty I was completely ignorant as to how I should manage to install them in the house with the consent of the occupiers, and yet prevent the latter from suspecting anything. No. 81, Rue Vaugirard, was at that time occupied by a master paviour, who had taken the whole of the house and the garden, and it was to him consequently that I must apply. I formed my plan during the walk. We reached the house at about nine in the evening, and I said to the paviour—

"I am assistant-chief of the detective force, and you are doubtless aware that we are daily called upon to hear the revelations of thieves, convicts, and others, who, by placing us on the track of robberies which are about to be committed, enable us to foil the plans of the criminals. I have been informed that to-night, or certainly one of the next nights, robbers intend to scale your garden-wall, break in through the ground-floor windows, plunder you, and perhaps do something worse. I have therefore brought these two gentlemen, who are police inspectors, and you will allow them to remain in your garden till they can arrest the burglars."

The frightened paviour stammered that he did not know me, and should like to refer the matter to the police commissioner. We therefore proceeded all four to that official, to whom I told the same story, and who took the opportunity to make a most pompous eulogium of the police.

My two men were installed in the garden by the paviour, who gave them bread and cheese and wine. Several nights passed, and, as may be supposed, the burglars did not come, but the luckless tenant, who was growing more and more frightened, had iron bars put up to all his ground-floor windows.

One fine morning the police authorities, accompanied by Robert and Bastien, under the guard of numerous agents, a doctor, and the grave-digger from Père la Chaise, arrived at the house; and the latter, to the great amazement of the master paviour, began to dig up his garden. We then explained to him why it had been thought requisite to keep watch, and what we had come to find.

The search, begun at the spot marked on the plan, led to no result, until Inspector Laporte, noticing the obstinacy with which Robert had remained on the same spot since the beginning of the operation, said roughly to him—

"Change your place! is the old woman holding you by the feet?"

At this unexpected remark, Robert started and turned pale; the ground on which he had been standing was dug up, and the grave-digger's pick soon penetrated into a cavity.

"We have it," he shouted.

In fact, a moment later, he discovered a female skeleton in a perfect state of preservation, having round its neck the rope employed in strangulation, and a gold ring on a finger of the left hand. Doctors Mare and Bois de Louy, Dumoutier the anatomist, and Orfila the chemist, proceeded to an examination of the skeleton, and declared their belief in an assassination.

In spite of the crushing weight of evidence, Robert and Bastien enjoyed the benefit of extenuating circumstances, and were only condemned to penal servitude for life.

CHAPTER VIII.

FIESCHI AND PEPIN.

In 1831, M. Gisquet was appointed Prefect of Police, and during his tenure of office up to 1836, rendered great services to government. After many disturbances, tranquillity seemed restored to the capital, and hence on July 28th, 1835, Louis Philippe reviewed the National Guard on the Boulevards in the presence of an immense crowd. Still every brow was not unclouded, every heart was not at ease, and any careful observer would have noticed amid the crowd police officer Tranchard, who, since eleven o'clock on the previous night, had been watching the Boulevards with eight agents, and examining every window.

The police had been informed that an infernal machine intended to kill the king had been constructed, that this machine was in one of the houses on the Boulevard St. Martin, near the Ambigu Theatre, and that it would explode at the moment when the king passed, and destroy a great number of persons in the disaster which it occasioned.

In order to prevent this attempt, a watch was set on

this boulevard, which had no result; for, as all the world knows, the machine, placed in a house on the Boulevard du Temple, exploded, and killed a great many persons, though without wounding Louis Philippe, who stood erect among the dead and dying.

The author of the crime had taken advantage of the first moment of confusion to attempt flight by the rear of the house, where he was arrested. He refused to give his name; but on August 2nd, it was discovered at the prefecture that it was Fieschi. A search was at once made in the charge-books of the second division, and it was discovered that a warrant had been out for some time for the arrest of Fieschi, who was mixed up in a fraud on the treasury, and that this warrant had been entrusted to me for execution.

I had gone home from my office at ten on the previous evening, with perfectly easy mind, for I was quite unaware of this fact; but at six the next morning one of my agents came to me.

"It appears," said he, "that the individual who made the attempt on the Boulevard du Temple, is a certain Fieschi, against whom you have held a warrant for some time; the prefectly and the solicitor-general wish to know why you did not have this man arrested."

I at once recognised the importance of this question, and calculated in an instant the enormous responsibility which would rest upon me, if I had been by my neglect the indirect and the involuntary cause of the crime. Truth to tell, this warrant had not attracted my attention any more than the couple of hundred others which I received every month from the police offices, and which remained locked up in an office drawer, while awaiting execution. Fortunately I had made strenuous efforts to discover this culprit, as was proved by six reports of the steps taken, which were attached to the warrant. The warrant and the reports were immediately forwarded to the police, who thus acquired a certainty that I had displayed no negligence.

A few days later, it was found that the gun barrels employed in making the infernal machine had been placed in a trunk and carried by Dubronet, a porter, to the lodgings of Fieschi's mistress, Nina Lassave, whose abode, however, it was impossible to discover. This porter was a Picard, in whom strength took the place of intelligence, and who might be fairly compared to those beasts of burthen which carry a load, without knowing for whom or to what spot. When examined about his job, he replied that he had carried a chest, contents unknown, to a garret-room in the Town Hall quarter, but he could neither point out the street nor the person to whom he had gone. This man was put in charge of three agents, who had orders to find out the house in which the trunk had been deposited.

At that period, the district of the Town Hall was covered with small streets that no longer exist, and which were all alike, being equally filthy and narrow, and formed a perfect labyrinth in which the honest and unintelligent porter lost himself, and his weak imagination was completely routed.

The search went on for two days without success. The inspectors and the porter had gone through every street in the neighbourhood of the Town Hall, and before each house they had asked him—"Is it here?" Each time the son of Picardy answered "No, I don't think so; it can hardly be that." The agents, wearied and losing all hope of success, came in to report their fruitless efforts, and I was in our chief's office when they did so. "Intrust the matter to me," I said to him, "you know that I am lucky, and perhaps I may be able to find the house."

"I hope so," he answered; "go and do your best."

We left the prefecture, and proceeded towards the Town Hall. On coming to the corner of the Rue du Long Pont, I asked the inspectors whether they had gone through it. "Of course," one of them answered, "and several times indeed," and so we passed it. We went all over the district, stopping at every house, and always receiving the same answer from our porter.

My inspectors were probably beginning to feel inwardly delighted at my want of success, when I resolved to continue my investigations without the porter; but before sending him to the nearest guard-room, I asked him one last question.

"Did you see a church in the street to which you carried the trunk?"

"No, sir, I do not remember it," he said.

As I only obtained useless answers from Dubronet, I ordered my agents to leave him at the guard-house in St. Jean Market, and come back to me as quickly as they could.

In going off, they proceeded along the Rue du Long Pont, and had not gone one hundred yards when our inspector ran back to tell me that the porter had just recognised No. 11 in that street as the one to which he had carried the trunk. The few words I had said to him about the church sufficed to arrange his recollections.

I hastened to the house indicated, where I found Dubronet and an agent waiting for me in the yard. The porter told us that for some days past a young woman, who perfectly answered the description, had been living in the fourth floor, and, moreover, he recognised the porter as having brought her a trunk. I went up to that floor, rapped, but there was no answer; I shouted, and the same silence continued;

I peeped through the keyhole, and saw a dress spread out upon the bed, which faced the door. I at once thought that Nina Lassave had committed suicide, and I was just going down to fetch a commissioner of police to break open the door, when I saw a girl on the lower landing. By her face, I at once knew that she was the person I wanted, and so I walked up to her. "Are you not," I said to her, "Mademoiselle Nina Lassave?" "Yes, sir," she answered; "I see what it is, you have come to arrest me. I am sorry that you came to-day, for I had determined to destroy myself to-night, either by poison or by throwing myself into the river." I went into her room, and the trunk in question was by the bed-side. I had at length found the object of my search! I left Nina Lassave under the guard of my two agents, and went at once to inform M. Joly, head of the municipal police, of the capture I had made. After complimenting me upon its importance, he added, "This arrest will give the authorities the key to the whole affair, and throw an entirely new light upon the investigations."

In truth, it was not till after the confrontation of Nina Lassave with Fieschi, that the latter consented to speak, and Pepin and Morey were arrested. I left M. Joly and returned to my agents; while waiting for the police commissioners, whom I had sent for to witness the searching of the room, I conversed with Nina

Lassave, and asked her, among other questions, whether she was sincerely attached to Fieschi.

"I!" she said—"I could never endure him. I will say more, I never felt anything but repugnance for him."

"And yet you were his mistress?"

"Oh! that is a long story. Fieschi was my mother's lover, and for that reason I heartily detested him; but as we all lived together, I must either put up with it, or leave my mother, which I did not like to do. Fieschi often told me of his love for me, and taking advantage of my mother's absence, he had pressed me to yield to him, but I always repulsed his proposals, and hoped that I had disgusted him by my refusals, when one day my mother absented herself for twenty-four hours owing to a quarrel they had, and I was left alone with him. In order to inspire me with more confidence, he did not speak to me about his love the whole day, and at about nine o'clock I went to bed us usual. My room was on the ground-floor with a window looking on the yard. I double-locked my door and went to bed, but at midnight, was startled from sleep by some one tapping at my window. 'Who is there?' I asked, without rising. 'It is I, little Nina,' Fieschi answered; 'open quickly, I implore you, open.' On my refusal, and a threat to call for help, he went away silently, and I fancied I had escaped with the fright, but great was my error, for at about two in the morning, I was again aroused by the sound of one of the windows being broken, and then I saw a hand thrust through, withdraw the bolt, and Fieschi leapt into my room. All this took place so rapidly that I had not even time to rise, and, dumb with surprise, I found myself at his mercy. Though I tried to defend myself, I was compelled to yield, and from that night, in spite of my tears and supplications, I was forced to be his mistress! He loves me to distraction, and might perhaps have rendered me happy if I had responded to his love; but, as I told you, I never felt aught but repugnance and hatred for him. The body yielded, but the heart has ever revolted."

Morey and Pepin were arrested, and a few days later the latter was taken from prison by a magistrate's order, and entrusted to M. Milliet, a police commissioner, and two agents, who were to take him to his own house to be present at the emptying of the cesspool, in which it was thought that he might have thrown weapons or compromising papers. The commissioners stood close to the nightmen, and examined with the most scrupulous attention all their movements, and Pepin was a little in the rear between the two agents. The opening of the cesspool was in the cellar under the shop, and at about one in the morning Pepin noticed that M. Milliet, exclusively occupied with his task, was paying no attention to him, while his two keepers, yielding to fatigue and the noisome exhalations, had fallen asleep. Then, collecting all his courage, he ascended in three strides the sixteen steps that led to his shop; and when the commissioner and the agents noticed the flight of their prisoner, he was already in a place of safety, where he hid himself so well that the search of the police was useless.

Still, Pepin, like so many others, found a Judas to betray him. And on September 14th, our chief was ordered by the prefect to accompany an informer, a friend of Pepin, who knew his hiding-place and had promised to procure him a passport. I also joined in the expedition with a dozen agents.

Our chief, Sergeant Fraudin, and the informer, got into a carriage and set off as scouts, while the other agents and myself followed them to Tournon in vans, and arrived there at four in the afternoon. During this time our scouts had gone some distance along the road to Belleyme farm, where Pepin was concealed; but as N——, the denouncer, stated that the moment was not propitious, and that they must return in a few days, they came back to join us. In order not to excite any suspicions, most of the agents had game bags and fowling pieces; but this fact led to conjectures, for the inhabitants of the little town did not know what to think of all these sportsmen, who seemed to have no sport, since they had in reality come on a man hunt. Consequently, I proposed to send on part of the agents to sleep at Rosoy. This matter being arranged, I called one of my sergeants, whom I knew not to be particularly courageous, and said to him,—

"It is arranged that we are to spend the night watching in the fields." At these words I saw a slight shudder pass all over him. "But," I continued, "as we should only arouse suspicions by all of us remaining here, six will be enough to watch, and you will go with the rest to Rosoy, sleep there, and wait for us."

Our coward, delighted at not having to spend the night in the open air, started at eight in the evening for Rosoy, and walked the two leagues, not only without murmuring, but apparently pleased with the favour. The morrow we picked them up as we passed, and returned to Paris. But the affair was only suspended for a while, and on the 18th of the same month we received orders to go to Meaux, and not arrive there before ten P.M. This time the denouncer was not with us, for the affair was of the highest importance to the police. As the first expedition had failed, the prefect himself took the management of the present one, and kept the informer with him in his carriage. A little way out of Claye they caught us up and passed us; and when we reached Claye our horses fell utterly exhausted, and we were compelled to hire post-horses.

At ten o'clock we reached Meaux, and at midnight started for Belleyme farm, which was about eight miles distant from Meaux. The gendarmes of the latter town accompanied us by the prefect's orders.

Pepin had been placed at this farm by a miller of Lagny, under the pretext that his feeble health required the fresh air and tranquillity of the country, and he had several times received visits here from his denouncer. On his last visit, N—— promised to bring Pepin a passport, by which he could escape to foreign parts; but instead of a passport he brought him death.

So soon as we reached the farm, after losing our way several times in the darkness, the mounted gendarmes guarded the walls, supported by a dozen police agents, so that no one could scale them unseen. At the same time the prefect, our chief, myself, and the rest of the agents, proceeded to the large entrance gate and knocked loudly.

After waiting some ten minutes the massive gates swung back on their rusty hinges. The prefect himself cross-examined farmer Rousseau, who replied to all the questions asked him, "I do not know this M. Pepin; I do not know what you mean." During this time, we had scattered through the different buildings, in order to search them simultaneously. As I carefully examined every nook and corner of a large hall I entered, Sergeant Fraudin entered an adjoining room and shouted, "Hilloh! here is a bed still warm; the occupant has not left it long!" At this exclamation I rushed into the room where he was. He had drawn away a bed and discovered a wall cupboard behind it, in which Pepin was standing in his shirt, with his back to the wall, and we requested him to come out. On finding himself captured, his first exclamation was to beg us not to hurt him; but seeing nothing in our behaviour to justify any such fear, he added, "You fancy, I suppose, that I am a Carlist? Well, you are mistaken, as I shall be fully able to prove hereafter."

The prefect came in; Pepin was ordered to dress; and we made a search, which led to no other result than finding a volume of St. Just on the night commode. This operation over, the prefect, accompanied by N——, went to his carriage and returned to Paris. We started leisurely with our prisoner. In our van were our chief, Pepin, three agents, and myself; and the remainder followed in another van.

In the former vehicle the conversation, during the whole journey, was gay and lively; and to listen to us nothing would have led to the supposition that there was among us a man reserved for the scaffold. At Claye we all breakfasted at the same table on omelettes and mutton cutlets. Pepin ate with good appetite;

and when he got into the vehicle again, talked the whole way from Claye to Paris about agriculture and drying vegetables. He told us about Prince de Rohan, who was also fond of agriculture, and a friend of his. "It's owing to my intimacy with that personage," he said, "that I am believed to be a legitimist."

I will not allude to the trial of Fieschi, Pepin, and Morey, as everybody knows it, and what the end was; but what may not be generally known, is that N——, the friend of Pepin—the confidant who was to procure him the means of escape—received a reward of 25,000 francs for the denunciation, and put the sum to such good account that, at this moment, he has a fine business and a handsome fortune.

Pepin constantly denied his complicity with the two other accused; and even on the scaffold, when he was being fastened to the fatal plank, he turned his head and exclaimed, "My friends, I am innocent! I die innocent!" Even when the knife was over his head just ready to drop, Pepin again cried, "I am innocent!"

At six o'clock that morning, his wife and four children collected in his bedroom, and kneeling before a crucifix, passed the day in asking Heaven to have pity on their tears, and be merciful to their father and husband!

CHAPTER IX.

THE CAZES MURDER.

"Help! murder! assassins!"—such were the cries that rang along the Neuilly road, at about nine in the evening of October 9, 1835, in dark and rainy weather. A young man fell with four dagger stabs; and although he cried several times for help—though he contrived, wounded as he was, to drag himself to the nearest houses and rap at the doors—the inhabitants, thinking that he was only a drunken man, were not at all affected by these cries. A few minutes later an omnibus passed, and the conductor, hearing the groans, stopped the conveyance and found the young man lying on the ground, and murmuring the words, "I am most unfortunate, I am wounded to death!" He raised him gently, placed him in his omnibus, and carried him to the nearest wine shop.

The unfortunate man had scarce been seated in a chair ere he expired, without having been able to utter a single word. His shirt, his clothes, the chair itself were saturated with the blood which poured copiously from his wounds—one in the chest, one in the right shoulder, the third in his left side, and the fourth in his back.

So soon as the prefecture was informed of the crime, the chief of the detectives went to the spot to commence an inquiry. The only proof of identification which he found upon the body was a Rouen diligence ticket merely bearing the name of Cazes. This ticket was at once sent to the prefecture with a report. The chief of the municipal police handed it to me, while ordering me to take all the necessary steps to detect the assassin.

In conformity with these orders I set to work, and soon learnt that an individual of the name of Cazes, a journeyman gunsmith, lived at No. 5, Rue de Valois-Batave. I then learned from the landlord of this house that his lodger, a very steady and respectable young man, had not been home for three days, a thing which had never happened before.

"However," he added, "Cazes occupies a room with one of his comrades, of the name of Dublé, also a gunsmith; but the latter does not come home till nine in the evening, and if you have any inquiries to make, he will probably be able to satisfy you."

"Where does this Dublé work?"

"I do not know."

I was thus reduced to wait till nine in the evening for the very problematical arrival of a young man, who might meet a friend on the way and not return till midnight, or perhaps not at all. This last reflection rendering me most impatient, I went to a reading-room in the Palais Royal, took the addresses of all the gunsmiths, and off I set, asking everywhere whether they knew a man of the name of Dublé.

"Oh, yes," one of the workmen at the shop in the Rue du Coq St. Honoré, said to me, "I know him, and he works at the shooting gallery in the Allée des Veuves."

I proceeded there at once and rightly found my Dublé repairing a brace of pistols. I did not think it safe to ask him any questions about the assassination of his comrade, through fear of committing an indiscretion which might prevent the success of the affair; moreover, I was completely ignorant of what might be going on at Neuilly. Hence I told Dublé that the prefect wished to see him directly, to ask him a few questions about a young man who had been arrested on the previous evening bearing prohibited arms, which he said he had obtained from a friend of his of the name of Dublé.

The gunsmith followed me without any difficulty; but a moment later asked me what the weapons were which had been seized upon the young man.

"They are cavalry pistols."

"And you say that he knows me?"

"He declares he is very intimate with you."

"Do you know his name?"

"No; I heard it mentioned, but I have forgotten it."

"What is he like?"

I gave him a description of my own in answer to this request. While conversing in this manner, we reached the prefecture, but, instead of leading him to the office I ordered two agents to take him to Neuilly, and confront him with the corpse, which he at once recognised. On his return to Paris Dublé was locked up at the depôt, and on being examined the next day, he stated very frankly that his comrade had started for Havre or Rouen, after confiding to him that he was only taking this journey to save the honour of one of the friends of his youth, who had asked him several times to cash bills at bankers, the last instance being at M. Lebœuf's, Rue Hauteville.

"I do not know the friend's name," Dublé added. "I only know that he is employed at the post-office or the customs—that he has a brother an officer, and that he lives in furnished apartments in the Rue des Vieux Augustins—I forget the number, but I should know the house again were I to see it."

Our chief, Dublé, and myself got into a cab, and soon arrived at the house which the gunsmith pointed out to us. The porter, on being spoken to, told us that the person we were inquiring for was a M. X——, who had certainly lodged in the house, but had gone away and not left his new address. "However," he added, "if you will wait a moment, I will see whether my mistress knows it." The latter lived on the first floor; the porter went up-stairs; we followed him and we heard him say, "Some gentlemen were asking for M. X——'s address, and I told them that I did not know it, as he requested me to do." Without hearing any more, our chief stepped forward, stated who he was, and reproached the landlady for aiding a criminal in trying to escape from justice. The terrified lady at once ordered the porter to tell the truth, and the latter, at once changing his note, informed us that X—— was a post-office clerk, that he lived with a woman who was of very expensive habits, and that he was now residing with her at No. 20, Rue de Tivoli.

After this visit, Dublé was taken back to the depôt, and I went to see M. Lebœuf, who told me that a few days back a young man answering exactly to the description of Cazes, had presented bills for payment. "I regret," he said to me, "that I paid them, for I have just learned that these bills were abstracted from a post letter." This last circumstance confirmed the presumption existing against X——; hence, on leaving the bankers, I proceeded straight to the general post-office. I applied to the head of a department, to whom I stated who I was, and the purpose of my coming. After arranging the excuse he should offer, he sent for X—— to his room.

"This gentleman," he said to him, "has come to ask you to be good enough to go with him to the magistrate, who only requires your evidence in order to set at liberty a young man, who says he is an intimate friend of yours, and who was arrested yesterday for an assault."

The pill was so well gilt that X—— swallowed it without difficulty. Still, as we went along, I was compelled to answer questions to some extent resembling those which Dublé had asked me two days previously, and to draw up another fictitious invention. It may be easily conjectured that once he was at the prefecture he remained there.

A search at his lodgings led to the discovery of a dagger with a blunt point, among other articles. When confronted with the corpse of Cazes he denied the murder, although the physicians declared that the dagger found at his lodging resembled in size the one which had struck the victim.

At the assizes, X—— continued his system of denial, and was only condemned to seven years' penal servitude for stealing money-letters, as the grand jury threw out the indictment for murder.

CHAPTER X.

THE MURDER OF HERMANCE DECREUS.

WE now come to a criminal who stands completely apart from the ordinary type : a robber with a charitable and good humane heart, who liked to relieve want out of his own pocket, who took advantage of the numerous accidents of his sad life to do good, and who yet ended by losing on the scaffold a head which society accursed, which humanity reproved, and which justice branded by stamping on the forehead the word "assassin."

Jadin, in 1833, kept, with his concubine Rosalie C——, a café in the Rue Saint Germain l'Auxerrois. Whatever may be the profits attaching to such a trade, whatever the chances of success a good connection may offer, Jadin was far from satisfied with his position ; hence he added to his legitimate trade the profits he derived from the far more lucrative profession of robbery.

An expert locksmith and clever workman, he excelled in the manufacture of false keys ; moreover, rare prudence secured him impunity for a long time

One day, however, being less fortunate than usual, he was caught in the act of robbery with false keys, to which was added the more serious offence of burglary. He was brought before the assizes and sentenced to ten years' penal servitude.

On the same day as Jadin was arrested, Rosalie asked permission to see her lover at La Force. M. B——, the clerk to whom she applied, representing herself to be Jadin's wife, was touched by her sorrow and her tears. B—— was young and Rosalie pretty, hence B—— obtained her the permission she required, and in exchange for his complaisance he soon achieved the reward which he desired, for close and intimate relations were established between them. Unfortunately, B——, with the thoughtlessness of lovers, could not separate his public from his private life, and his new mistress soon knew the most private secrets of his daily work at the Palace of Justice.

Thanks to this information, which Rosalie faithfully reported to Jadin in prison, the latter was informed that a police-note was appended to his indictment, proving that at a former period he had been sentenced to ten days' imprisonment for an assault. Now this note, which was not very serious in itself, offered one remarkable fact, which might prove very prejudicial to the accused. Jadin was described in it as a "journeyman locksmith," and this trade coinciding with the charge of committing robbery by the aid of false keys, might give additional force to the evidence and proofs already collected. It was highly important then to Jadin that this note should be destroyed, and all his wishes, and all the intrigues of his concubine tended to this object.

B——, who was necessarily assailed by Rosalie with tears, threats, and seductions, could only secure peace by giving her the incriminating document, which was at once taken to Jadin and destroyed by him. B——, however, afraid lest this abstraction might be noticed and himself rendered responsible for it, asked for a duplicate at the prefecture, under the excuse that the first copy had gone astray. The duplicate requested was made out by a clerk of the name of Benoit, but the dangerous words "journeyman locksmith" were omitted from the second copy. No one ever knew whether this omission was forgetfulness or premeditation on the part of Benoit; but public opinion inclined to the latter theory, because he committed suicide shortly after.

Jadin was tried and sentenced to ten years' penal servitude, but Rosalie induced her lover to make revelations, so as to obtain the favour of not being sent to the hulks, but serve his time in the Paris prisons, where he would suffer less and she could easily see him. For this object she at once informed the police of all the details of the abstracted note, which led first to B——'s dismissal and then to his arrest. Jadin, on his side, revealed to the police that he committed the robbery of one hundred and twenty-four silver forks and spoons, and one hundred and eighteen drinking cups of the same metal, at the Morin seminary in the Rue de la Pepinière, and mentioned as his accomplices two men of the name of Fréchard and Liekens. Then he added that his brother-in-law, G——, a professor at that school, had supplied him with the impressions for the false keys, and all the requisite information for effecting the robbery.

The three accomplices were arrested and there was another trial. Fréchard and Liekens were acquitted for want of corroborative evidence, but G—— was sentenced to four years' imprisonment, while the denouncer had twelve years' penal servitude added to his original sentence.

Four years after, owing to his revelations and the services he had rendered the police, and in consideration of his good conduct in prison, Jadin received a full pardon. So soon as he was set at liberty, the unhappy man, who was really resolved to give up the wretched life he had so long led, paid a visit to the chief of the detective force, and thanked him, with tears in his eyes, for all the kindness shown him. He added, that he was promised constant work as locksmith, and being now certain of earning his bread honestly, he meant to give up entirely his habits of sloth and debauchery, and shun his old comrades of perdition—in a word, he vowed that his conduct should henceforth be irreproachable. And Jadin was really honest and industrious during three months; he was even beginning to display a religious feeling, when, unhappily, he met Seguin and Valhin, ex-convicts and thorough scoundrels with whom he had previously "worked." He was obliged to talk, describe his mode of life, his occupation and means of existence; but the two villains, on hearing their ex-comrade describe his yesterday's toil and his morrow's intentions, instead of blushing at their own reprobate existence, received this confession with atrocious jeers and infamous jests. They strove to prove to Jadin that manual labour was only good for brutes and imbeciles, and that a man, a clever man especially, ought not to work from morn till night for three francs. They flashed some jewellery in his eyes and rattled some gold coins at his ear; and they reminded him of his past successes and the revels they had enjoyed together, arousing in turn his vanity, his indolence, and his love of pleasure and good cheer. They easily destroyed in a few hours all the good resolutions which four years of imprisonment, privations, and mental struggling had so laboriously formed.

From this day Jadin gave up work to return to his

old habits, and buried himself deeper and deeper in the mire from which he had momentarily emerged; but amid all his crimes he frequently had one of those impulses of humanity which denote a generous nature and compassionate heart. Two facts I will quote furnish a sufficient proof of this.

One day he entered a house in the Place Royale and went upstairs in search of an adventure. He came to a door, at which he rapped, but received no answer; he knocked a second time, and as the silence continued he employed a false key and went in. But at the sight of the furniture he stood stupified. Paper measures hanging on a nail told him that the room belonged to a dressmaker, while the furniture consisted of a wretched bed, a worm-eaten chest of drawers, and a few rickety chairs. On the mantelpiece was a cage with a canary, whose seed-box was quite empty, while the fountain was full of clear fresh water; everything announced want, but was perfectly clean and tidy. "Heaven forgive me!" he exclaimed; "the person I wanted to rob is as poor as Job," and feeling in his pockets, he took out the only two five-franc pieces he possessed, laid them upon the cage, and went away.

Another time, Jadin was in the Rue du Rocher, and stopped before a mean-looking house. Confiding, however, in the popular adage that "the hood does not make the monk," he went up four flights of narrow, damp, and dark stairs; there was a door facing him, and, after knocking several times, he entered by means of false keys. Here, again, the sight of the interior did not answer his expectations; there were a mattress and a wretched set of drawers as the sole furniture, and he found an old coat, a pair of poor sheets, and a police-book belonging to a journeyman hatter. He gazed sadly at this miserable attic, in which there was not even a chair. All at once a paper lying on the chimney-piece caught his eye; it was a notice to quit, unless the tenant at once paid twenty francs owing rent. "Really," he said, "here is a man more wretched than myself." He only took a moment to learn the landlord's name, as well as that of the tenant, and then he proceeded straight to the former.

"Here, sir," he said, "are twenty francs which your tenant, M. Durand, requested me to pay you, while begging you to withdraw your notice. Be kind enough to give me a receipt."

He went away, placed the receipt in an envelope, and sent it by post to the hatter. Such facts require no comment; but, alas! these good instincts were destined to lead to his destruction!

At six in the morning of January 12, 1838, a violent ring at my bell announced a visitor; it was police inspector Roger, who came to inform me that a girl had been assassinated on the previous evening in her room at No. 41, Rue des Petites Ecuries. On hearing of this, our chief at once went to the spot; but not having been able to obtain any useful information he requested me to continue the investigation in his place. I at once went to the address, and cross-questioned the portress.

The victim, Hermance Decreus, lady's-maid to a Madame Widmer, had leave from her mistress to go out, and on the very day of her deplorable end had arranged to go for a walk at two o'clock with her lover, a man-servant of the name of Mercier, engaged in another family. She went up to her bedroom on the fifth floor, and a few minutes later an individual passed the porter's lodge and went up-stairs without saying a word. The portress ran out to ask him where he was going, but as the man mumbled a name which she fancied she recognised as that of one of her tenants, she returned to her lodge without troubling herself further. A quarter of an hour later the stranger slowly came down-stairs again, and in passing the lodge thrust the fore-finger of his left hand into his ear, so as to conceal his face as much as he could. This man had also been seen, but not particularly noticed, by M. Mestro, who had come to pay a visit to the Widmers. At three o'clock Mercier arrived. Impatient like all lovers, he ran up-stairs, found the bedroom door ajar, thrust it open in the hope of surprising the girl, and was himself greatly surprised at finding everything in disorder. He turned round to ask for an explanation, and in a room facing that of Hermance he saw the unhappy creature lying on the ground in a pool of blood. At Mercier's cries, the portress hurried up, and the victim was removed to her bed, where she expired, before she was able to describe her murderer. The disorder in Hermance's room proved that a struggle had taken place. The ill-fated girl had three deep wounds in the neck, and the physicians summoned to make the autopsy declared that the wounds had been made by a heavy turn-screw, which the murderer left on the scene of the crime.

Such were the events which the portress had just told me, when the magistrate and the police commissioner arrived. The latter, on seeing me, at once said, 'I believe that you are losing your time here; there is nothing to be done; and the portress has been able to give but a very indistinct description of the murderer. Besides, your chief came yesterday, and he plainly saw that the culprit is not to be found in this house."

"That may be very true," I replied; "but I have received orders and must perform them. I am here and shall remain here." With these words, I turned on my heel and saluted M. Legonidec, the magistrate, who received me most warmly, and said: "I hope, Monsieur Canler, that you are about to remain with me and aid me in my researches." I at once placed myself at his disposal, and began by obtaining as accurate a description of the man as I could. The portress and her daughter had since seen his face; they only noticed that he wore very short moustaches, and this indication was far from satisfactory. Taking the turnscrew left in the room by the murderer, I ordered an agent to go to every ironmonger's shop in the capital, if necessary, and discover where it was made and to whom it was sold. On the second day my efforts were crowned with success, and I knew that it was sold by a M. Michon, at No. 39, Rue du Petit Carreau.

I went to this tradesman and learned from him that he had sold the turnscrew on December 31, for 1 franc 10 cent., to an individual whose description answered tolerably well to the vague indications given by the portress in the Rue des Petites Ecuries. I then proposed to my chief to arrest all the malefactors whom I supposed capable of committing such a crime. It was a rather general measure, but one that circumstances fully justified. Several arrests were made, but the confrontation with the witnesses led to no result.

The affair was in this state and success seemed

dubious, when, on January 12th, while passing, at about five in the evening, along the Rue Pont Louis Philippe, I saw Jadin, Valhin, and Rose Guibert and her sister, two oyster women, come out of a café. They stopped on the pavement to talk, the men facing the house, the women with their backs to it. I was compelled to pass between the latter and the wall, but the passage was so narrow that I was obliged to move sideways; very naturally, my eyes fell on the two men facing me, and I was at once struck by the resemblance between Jadin and the man described as the murderer of Hermance Decreus. As for Jadin he looked at me without bowing or seeming to notice me. Still I did not think myself justified in arresting him immediately for several reasons: 1, the only charge I had was this resemblance, which was probably deceitful. 2, as I said, on leaving prison, he manifested such repentance and religious sentiment, that the police could not believe that he was the assassin. In any case, the good opinion entertained of him rendered him perfectly secure, and I felt quite sure of being able to arrest him, whenever it might be necessary. I reported to my chief and then went to the Rue des Petites Ecuries.

"Do you recognise me?" I asked the portress.

"Yes, sir; you came here at the time of the assassination of that poor Hermance."

"Now, madam, be good enough, as well as your daughter, to give me your closest attention. I am about to give you a description of the man whom I believe to be the murderer."

I then described Jadin to them, from head to foot: his face, the size of his head, the manner in which he wore his hat, his step; and at each trait the women replied, "Oh, it is he! it is he!"

Sure of my part, I returned to my chief, and we proceeded together to the magistrate, who issued warrants against Jadin and Valhin, who were both at once arrested. During the examination, however, we learned that on January 17, the very day on which the murder was committed, Jadin had been in the company of one Fréchard, called Brutus, who had acquired a certain reputation in the thieves' world through his dexterity, and the confession which Lacenaire and Avril had made to him of their intention to kill Widow Chardon and her son. In fact, Fréchard, when called as witness during the trial of that melancholy business, openly avowed that he had been cognizant of that criminal project. In the face of such antecedents, and remembering, too, that he had been in prison with Jadin, and pardoned at the same time, it was thought highly probable that he might have been an accomplice, and a warrant was also issued against him.

So soon as Jadin was arrested he was taken before the magistrate, who sent for the three persons who had described the assassin; but, incredible to relate, not one of them positively recognised the man whom I had discovered solely from the imperfect descriptions which they had given me of him. Hence, taking advantage of the indecision of the three principal witnesses, Jadin adopted at the trial a system of complete denial. He was, for all that, condemned to death. Fréchard, found guilty of complicity in robbery alone, was sentenced to ten years' imprisonment.

On the day previous to this trial, Jadin was acquitted on a charge of robbery, in complicity with Valhin and Seguin, who were sentenced as relapsed convicts, the first to twenty-four, the second to twenty years' penal servitude.

As Jadin refused to appeal to the Court of Cassation, the interval between sentence and execution was exhausted, and the next day the unhappy man would expiate with his blood the crime which he had committed. The chief and myself went to see him at the Conciergerie, and found him sitting in a corner of his cell, attentively reading a catechism. He raised his head, bowed to us, and thanked us for our visit.

"Why did you not appeal?" we asked him.

"Oh, gentlemen, death is a hundred-fold preferable to the frightful existence which I should now lead.

Life is a burden to me, and I certainly shall do nothing to prolong it. The hapless girl whom I stabbed, and whose blood plashed me, is ever present to my mind. At night I see her in dreams—and what dreams, great Heaven! By day, I fancy I still see her, and this bleeding image rises before me to reproach me with my crime, my cowardly cruelty. Oh no, I was not born to be an assassin!

"On January 1," he continued, "Fréchard, with whom I had been in prison, came to me and wished me a happy new year. One politeness deserves another, and so I took him to breakfast with me in the Rue de l'Arcade. He talked and drank, and after breakfast I proposed to him to accompany me to La Roquette prison, where my brother-in-law was detained.

"'I would do so with pleasure," Fréchard replied, 'but I cannot, and will not, be seen with you in my present wretched condition.'

"'Is it only that? Come with me, and I will get you clothes and money in a very short time.'

"Our heads were heated with wine, and walking haphazard we reached the Rue des Petites Ecuries.

"'There,' I said, pointing to No. 41, 'is a fine house in which there are rich families, and consequently servants. I will pay a visit to the bedroom of one of them. Wait for me here; I shall not be long.'

"I boldly entered the house, and went up the stairs. The portress ran after me to ask me where I was going; but I mentioned the first name that occurred and reached the fifth floor without any obstacle. I had a turn-screw about me, and in a second I forced a lock, which was as bad as all those on servants' doors. I searched the furniture, and made up the bundle which I intended to carry off; but at this moment I turned round, and saw a girl in the doorway, who began crying 'Thieves!' I rushed toward her, stopped her cries by pressing my hand on her mouth, and said, 'Silence, for your own sake—silence. I have been tried and sentenced before, and if I am caught now it is all over with me. Silence, or you are a dead woman!' This threat intimidated her, and she let me go; but I had only gone down a few steps when she began screaming again. Oh, then! a cloud of blood passed before my eyes, I saw in perspective the assizes and the hulks, and, in order to escape this frightful vision, I rushed upon the girl, dragged her into a room facing her own, and threw her down, placing my knee on her chest and holding her neck with my left hand; then, with my other hand, I felt in my pocket, drew out a knife with a very narrow blade, and after opening it with my teeth, buried it thrice in her neck. This deed done, I went down with a great affectation of calmness, and found Fréchard. You know the rest. But you must allow that the doctors are precious donkeys, for they all declared that the wounds were made with the turnscrew which I left in the poor girl's room."

On the next day, that of the execution, I stationed myself, as usual, at the foot of the scaffold. Jadin, on getting out of the coach said to me, suppliantly, "Monsieur Canler, will you embrace me?"

"Here?" I said. "What can you be thinking of? It is impossible."

"Jadin, who had listened with resignation to the consoling words of the Abbé Montès, calmly mounted the steps of the scaffold, surrendered himself into the hands of the assistant executioner without any affectation or weakness, and a minute later the work of expiation was accomplished.

Jadin was two-and-thirty years of age, five feet two in height, with a fresh, ruddy face, and a tendency to corpulence, but on the whole a good-looking fellow. A clever workman, he might have secured a modest, honourable existence; but his taste for indolence and pleasure insensibly led him to seek in robbery the means to defray his expenses. Once repentant, he relapsed into crime, through his fatal meeting with the two men with whom he had been in prison. Had it not been for this, he would have probably persevered in the honourable course which he began after his liberation. This is an irrefragable example of the necessity for every man who has been punished by the law to break off absolutely with all those with whom he may come in contact while expiating his faults.

CHAPTER XI.

THE APRIL FOOL.

"HELP yourself, and Heaven will help you!" This old axiom, which goes back to the time of the Apostles, must be applied more frequently by the police than by any one else. Appointed to seek criminals; forced to foil the machinations of malefactors, whose principle it is how to escape from surveillance; constrained to grope his way without any certain data, information, or traces, the police agent must ever help himself, and feel only too happy if Heaven respond to his appeal.

I had learned that Pageot, the master of that lodging-house where Lacenaire, François, and so many other celebrated criminals had put up, had been sheltering for some time past a clever professional thief of the name of C——, who committed robberies with false keys, in the company of L——, an ex-convict, G——, and Angelique, L——'s concubine.

It was principally on Sundays, at the hour when retired gentlemen, merchants, and clerks leave their apartments to breathe the country air or swell the crowd on the public walks, that C—— and his worthy associates left their lurking place to go and collect their honey, like industrious bees. I knew the address of C——, but not that of his accomplices; I therefore ordered four agents to watch his movements, and catch him in the act, were it possible.

"As this is Sunday," I said to them, "C—— will probably employ it to commit some new robbery. You will follow him, so as not to be seen; and you may, perchance, catch the whole party in the same haul;" and then, addressing one of the agent's associates, I said to him, "You will direct the affair, and I shall make you responsible for its success."

"It's all very easy talking, M. Canler," the man replied, "but we do not know C——; and the fellow is sure to be on his guard. If we only show the end of our noses, he will see them; and then good-bye to the affair."

"What day of the month is it?" I asked, after a little reflection.

"April 1st."

"Well, you must take advantage of it, and play our robbers a trick, by availing yourself of the well-known custom of the day."

"How so?"

"Very simply: you will send a porter to tell him that his friend Charles is waiting for him to come and eat a chop with him at the wine-shop at the corner of the Rue St. Martin. Very probably C—— will come to see who this friend is, and you will be able to see what he looks like. Good morning."

In conformity with this plan, my agents sent a porter to the thief, who hurried in his shirt-sleeves to the wine-dealer's, and asked—

"Where is the friend who has asked me to breakfast?"

"What friend?" the landlord inquired.

"I don't know. A porter has just been to me to tell me that my friend Charles was waiting for me here to crack a bottle and eat a chop."

"Ah, ah!" the landlord replied, with a laugh; "you didn't think of the first of April, eh? Why, you've been made a fool of."

"Well, that is true," C—— said, in the same light tone; "I have been really taken in, I allow."

Then he returned to his lodgings, which he did not leave till eleven o'clock, when he proceeded straight to No. 140, Rue St. Denis.

The agents, who followed him at a distance, placed themselves in adjacent passages to await his coming out. After a two hours' sentry so, they saw him returning with the three persons described as his accomplices. One of these men was dressed in blouse and cap; the other in a sleeve-waistcoat and cap, as was G——; and Angelique had a basket on her arm.

All four proceeded towards the Pont Neuf, which they crossed, and sat down on the steps of the Mint to hold a council of war. At length, the party started again; and, on reaching No. 43, Rue des Pères, the three men went in, while Angelique kept watch on the pavement. The agents, concealed in different gateways, waited for forty minutes, and then saw these thieves who had entered the house in blouses and caps, leave it in frockcoats and hats, and, moreover, loaded with immense bundles. Angelique joined them, and all four preceeded to the Quay Malaquais. They had scarce reached it ere the agents dashed upon them, and tried to master them; but they had to do with tough fellows. The thieves, who had a prospect of penal servitude for life, defended themselves like lions, and turned every possible thing into an offensive weapon. One of the agents, in order to intimidate C——, with whom he was rolling on the ground, was compelled to draw a pistol and threaten to blow out his brains.

At the moment when this desperate contest was taking place, M. Delessert, Prefect of Police, who was riding about the capital, according to his usual custom, passed along the quay, and was able to convince himself of the zeal and devotion which his agents displayed in the performance of their duty.

The guard soon hurried up. Police agents and

thieves were picked up out of the gutter, and marched in company to the guard-house, where the captured bundles were examined. They contained, in addition to a large quantity of body and bed linen, two overcoats, six frockcoats, handkerchiefs, a gold watch and chain, two diamond studs, a clock, &c., all belonging to a gentleman of property, who spent every Sunday in the country.

Angelique, who had twenty false keys in her basket, was sentenced to five years' penal servitude, C—— and G—— to seven, and L——, as a relapsed convict, for life.

C——, as he said, had reason to remember April fool-day.

CHAPTER XII.

THE SÉCHEPINE MURDER.

On the morning of June 11th, 1843, some promenaders discovered, a short distance from the walk called La Belle Etoile, the naked body of a man recently and imperfectly hidden in a clump of trees. A few yards further on, a pool of blood, which attempts had been made to cover with handfuls of sand and grass, attested that the murder had been committed there. Lastly, blood-stained clothes, and a hammer, doubtless left by the assassin, were discovered close at hand.

The numerous wounds with which the body was covered, and the fractures of the skull, indicated that the hammer was the chief instrument of the crime. The pockets of the clothes were searched, but nothing was found except a small note, on which was written the words, "In order to have a good number, you must say three Paters and three Aves." The victim was then conveyed to the Morgue.

The agent Palestrino was sent to the spot to make an investigation; but, as he was unable to collect any information that would place him on the track of the assassin, he contented himself with sending in a negative report. I could not understand the indifference of this agent; for I had always thought that, when an assassination occurred, the police ought never to relax in their efforts; so I went to report the facts to my chief, and I asked him whether he thought that the discovery of the criminal ought to be left to an accident more or less remote?

"Certainly not," he said; "there is always something to be done."

"Well, are you willing that I should take it in hand?"

"Yes: devote yourself exclusively to this affair."

It was eleven in the morning. I selected two agents, and I set out, deeply engaged in thought. The victim was young; there was no paper to prove his identity; but the little note found in his pocket led me to presume that the unhappy fellow might have been employed in some matters of military substitution, or be himself a recruit. I thought that he might have come from one of the low brothels on the Vincennes road, which was near the scene of the murder, and that he had been killed by some of the wretched frequenters of those houses. Supplied with the description of the victim, I went to all the tolerated houses in the vicinity of the Barrière du Trône to inquire whether any young man answering the description I gave had been seen there; but all the answers were negative. I then sent for two fiacres, into which I bundled all the mistresses and women of these houses, and sent them to the Morgue, but not one of them recognised the body. While this was taking place, a young man came in and told me that the corpse was that of one of his townsmen of the name of Séchepine. Taking advantage of this valuable information, I minutely had this name looked for at the lodging-houses' police-office, where was found, "Séchepine, twenty-four years of age, man-servant, born in the department of the Meurthe, went on the 10th to lodge at No. 33, Rue Philippeaux."

I proceeded to this address, and asked the landlady whether Séchepine was still lodging with her.

"No, sir," she answered; "he came in on Saturday and left on Sunday at nine in the morning."

"Pardon me, madam," I replied, "but you must be mistaken; for it is impossible, for solid reasons, that Séchepine could have left you at nine o'clock on Sunday morning. Be good enough, pray, to reflect."

I could safely affirm this; for the corpse had been found at seven A.M.,—that is to say, two hours prior to Séchepine's asserted departure.

"I assure you, sir, that I am not mistaken." And to give me a proof, she called her daughter, and said—

"Just come here, and tell us exactly on what day

and at what hour that gentleman, whose name I would not tell you, left the house."

"Why, mamma, you know very well that it was at nine o'clock on Sunday morning."

This second assertion staggered me. Still, I continued—

"During Séchepine's short stay with you, did he speak to you about any of his acquaintances?"

"No, sir; he merely said that my house was recommended to him by a person of the name of Drouin, a substitute in an artillery regiment, who lodged with us some time ago."

"When that soldier lived in your house, did he receive any visitors?"

"I never saw anybody but a M. Boutin, who lives in the Passage de la Marmite, and for whom Séchepine told me that he had worked."

"I went to this M. Boutin and asked him whether Séchepine had been employed in his yard."

"I never heard the name," he said to me.

"Do you know Drouin, an artilleryman?"

"Oh, yes, very well indeed; and he is now, I think, at Vincennes."

Then, after reflecting a while, he added—

"I employed for some time a young man who had worked in the boat building trade at Joigny."

"What is his name?"

"I forget; but he left here an unsealed letter which he had intended to send his father."

"Can I see it?"

"Oh, certainly."

This letter was signed "Salmon."

Feeling persuaded that the three persons whom I had questioned were mistaken, and that Salmon was no other than Séchepine, I requested one of M. Boutin's workmen to be good enough to accompany me to the Morgue; but this man did not recognise the corpse as that of his old comrade. I sent one of my inspectors to the lodging-house in the Rue Philippeaux to fetch the landlady, who confirmed the workman's statement by declaring that she neither recognised the face nor the clothes shown her, and that neither applied to the individual who slept at her house on the night between the Saturday and the Sunday. She gave me his description, which corresponded with that given me by M. Boutin. I therefore concluded that the individual who slept at the Rue Philippeaux must be Salmon, and that he had taken Séchepine's papers after murdering him, hoping in this way to conceal the identity of the murderer under the name of the victim.

I was just going to leave the Morgue, when a young man came up to me and told me that he recognised the corpse as that of one Séchepine.

"We were born," he said, "in the same village, and

lived together at No. 1, Rue des Blancs Manteaux. On Saturday last he left me to go and try to get a situation at an office for servants at No. 1, Rue Grenetat, and I have not seen him again since until I unfortunately found him here."

This information permitted me to hope that I might at length follow the trail of the fellow whom I was seeking. I sent agents to watch the lodging in the Rue Philippeaux, and to the Passage de la Marmite, to arrest Salmon, should he present himself at either. Then I hurried to the keeper of the servants' register office in the Rue Grenetat, and learned that Séchepine had really been there on the Saturday to obtain a situation, and had left with a man who called himself Salmon, who said he could get him a situation at Nogent in the same family in which he served. I also learned that Salmon and his victim did not set out till nightfall. This, then, was what had occurred. Salmon had taken with him the hammer found on the scene of the murder. On reaching the Bois de Vincennes, he took advantage of the isolation and darkness to fell his companion, and as the latter still breathed, he finished him with his knife, after which he dug a hole with his hammer, which was not deep enough to conceal the body. He stripped it entirely of the clothes, and covered it with grass, sand, and leaves.

After setting my men to watch, I went with two agents to the Fort of Vincennes, for the purpose of arresting Drouin, the artilleryman, whom I suspected at the time of being an accomplice of Salmon. But the adjutant, to whom I applied, made ineffectual inquiries, and assured me that this artilleryman, who was entirely unknown at Vincennes, might be quartered at the military school. In consequence, I gave my two agents orders to proceed at once to those barracks and arrest Drouin, and myself returned to Paris. I then found myself led by the course of my investigations to the lodging-house in the Rue Philippeaux, and the agents on the watch assured me that Salmon had not made his appearance. Thence I proceeded to Madame Boutin, who told me that Salmon had been there in a cabriolet to ask her to lend him fifteen francs, but she had refused, and he had gone off again in his coach. During this time the agents appointed to watch the passage had gone to have some refreshments with their companions in the Rue Philippeaux. I went and questioned the beadle of the passage to try and obtain some information, but I could not have fallen on a worse man. Though I pressed him, he could not tell me the colour of the cab or of the horse, or its number. He was even ignorant whether the cab was hired from a stand or a stable, and he invariably answered every question, "I do not know, sir; I did not notice; I paid no attention; I do not remember."

"But tell me," I said to him, "did the driver get off his box?"

"Oh—yes—I recollect; and he even seemed to be in a great passion."

"Did he speak to you?"

"No, sir; but when he had lit his pipe, I heard him grumbling between his teeth, 'There's an animal; he hired me this morning at the Barrière de Grenelle; he owes me fifteen francs, and after making me drive about all day, he hasn't a farthing to pay me with.'"

This indication was a flash of light for me. It was nine in the evening. I returned to the prefecture, selected four agents, and we set out for Grenelle; and there, going from drinking-shop to drinking-shop, we made the most minute and useless inquiries up to the closing of these houses. At half-past eleven, as I was preparing to return to Paris, sorrowful at the ill-success of my enterprise, I perceived in the distance a gendarme who was just returning home after going round his district. On seeing him a fortunate inspiration occurred to me; I ran up to him, and, after telling him who I was, I asked him whether he had heard anything about a quarrel between an individual and a cab-driver, to whom the former owed a certain sum of money for his day's hire.

9

"Yes," he answered; "there is at this moment in the guard-room a person whom a driver gave in charge for not paying him."

Ten minutes later I had made myself known to the officer of the guard, and the prisoner was brought from his cell, where he was fast asleep, into my presence.

"What is your name?" I asked him.

"Séchepine," he replied, boldly.

"Where are your papers?"

"I have lost them."

"That is false." And looking him in the face, I added, as I laid a stress upon every word, "You are Séchepine's assassin."

The most skilful observer could not have noticed the slightest alteration on his face; he, however, was going to reply, but I cut him short by saying, "I will prove to you that I am well informed. On leaving the servants' register-office in the Rue Grenetat, you went to the Bois de Vincennes, where you assassinated Séchepine, and after stealing his papers, you went to the lodging-house in the Rue Philippeaux, where you entered your victim's name as your own. You worked with a M. Boutin, Passage de la Marmite; you were arrested at Joigny for committing a burglary and stealing a sum of one thousand francs; you escaped from the gendarmes, and as you must have papers at any cost to conceal your identity, you seized those of the unhappy man whom you assassinated."

"All that you say is perfectly true, excepting what relates to the murder of Séchepine, whom I do not know and never saw. As for the papers I handed to the lodging-house keeper, I found them in the street."

I had him stripped by my agents. The shirt which he was wearing had large spots of blood on the chest and the back; it was marked with Séchepine's initials, and it was the very shirt the assassin had taken off his victim.

"Whence come these blood stains?" I asked him.

"I bled at the nose."

"How can a bleeding at the nose have stained the back of your shirt? Explain that."

"I don't know; but it came from my nose all the same."

"Where did you get these two white handkerchiefs and waistcoat, which are stained with blood like the shirt?"

"I bought them for twenty sous of a man in the street."

I made Salmon dress himself again; and at midnight I took him to the prefecture in a fiacre. During the journey he slept soundly. The prefect, on being informed of this arrest, ordered me to return at once to Grenelle, and have a report drawn up by the police commissioner as to the seizure of the blood-stained clothes. I went to fetch Salmon from the depôt, where he was again fast asleep. In the fiacre he still slept; and he also slept while the commissioner was drawing up his report. On returning to Paris he was asleep again, almost before he got into his cell. On the morrow he confessed his crime, and related all the circumstances of this horrible murder.

I should have nothing to add to the preceding, were I not bound to note a peculiar fact which caused the death of the unhappy Séchepine, for another man had been originally selected as the victim. Salmon had introduced himself to the register-office keeper as a servant at Nogent, who had been sent by his master to engage another man. Now, on the day prior to the crime, he had arranged with a young man, a journeyman hairdresser, living in the Rue Popincourt, that on the next day the latter should come to the office at three in the afternoon, provided with his papers, and that Salmon would take him to his master. The hairdresser not having made his appearance, Salmon displayed the greatest annoyance, declaring that his master would be extremely angry at this delay. It was then that he proposed to Séchepine, who had come to look for a place, to accompany him to Nogent. The proposal was eagerly accepted, and we know what happened.

Salmon was dark, short, but very powerfully built, and his deep-set eyes added to the harshness of a naturally ferocious glance. He seemed utterly deprived of intellect, and the savage instincts of the brute were alone developed in him. He displayed on the scaffold the same stoicism which he had shown during the whole period of his arrest and trial. This man, who, under the weight of a capital accusation, did not find in himself sufficient energy, or an instinct of self-preservation, to keep awake, is probably the only one who ever had the "savageness" to place on his own flesh the still warm and blood-stained shirt of the wretched man whom he had just murdered. I do not believe that there is any other instance of such an assassination, in so far as it was accomplished like an ordinary act of life, without the slightest passion. And what was the object? To obtain the police-book of a working man!

CHAPTER XIII.

THE SÉNÉPART MURDER.

On December 6th, 1843, M. Virgile Sénépart, whose father had been a contractor to the Imperial armies, director of the Ambigu Theatre, and Colonel of the sixth legion of the National Guard, after the Revolution of 1830, came with tears in his eyes to inform the chief of the detective department that his mother, the widow Sénépart, residing at No. 24, Boulevard du Temple, had been strangled in her rooms on the second floor, and that numerous blows had been dealt upon the victim's head with a blunt instrument. The murder could not have been committed for the sake of vengeance, as some 1000 or 1200 francs, both in gold and silver, had been stolen from a desk, which was broken open for the purpose.

M. Sénépart told us that his suspicions were directed to a young man from Toulouse, of the name of Pagès or Magnès, of whom he gave a description. This young man had arrived in Paris some days previously. On the evening prior to the crime he called on Madame

Sénépart, to give her news of her nieces, and then went to M. Virgile to deliver to him a letter from his paternal uncle, a retired major of artillery, who resided at Toulouse.

The names of Pagès and Magnès were immediately sought for at the lodging houses, and at eight o'clock on the same evening a M. Pagès was arrested; but as the son of the victim did not recognise him as the person whom he suspected, he was set at liberty again.

Our chief, accompanied by his agents, went to the apartments of the murdered woman, to try and obtain some clue that might place him on the track of the culprit. As he was unable to collect any information, he went to the diligence offices to verify the way-bills; and as none of them contained the names mentioned by M. Sénépart, M. Allard sent in a report, which acknowledged himself beaten, and the next day I was ordered to pursue the investigation alone. For this purpose, I proceeded to the scene of the crime, to examine the locality and interrogate the house-porter. The description of the person whom he suspected to be the murderer tallied exactly with that given by M. Sénépart, and as a final peculiarity, the porter added, that he wore a coat lined with plaid silk. I went up to Madame Sénépart's rooms, in which her corpse was still lying; but as the magistrate was waiting there for the arrival of the doctor to undertake the autopsy, I could do nothing, and went away. I had brought with me an excellent friend, who did not belong to the police, and who waited for me at the door.

"I must go and see M. Sénépart," I said to him, "with whom I have been acquainted for a long time. I may obtain from him some useful information which may serve me as a starting-point."

I found the unhappy gentleman in a state of suffering difficult to describe.

"Ah! Monsieur Canler," he exclaimed, "as you know me, come to my help. Can you believe that people have aggravated the sorrow I am enduring by insinuating that I had my mother assassinated, in order to free myself from the annuity of 1500 francs which I pay her? It is abominable, is it not? My poor mother, whom I loved so dearly! Ah! I beg you, I implore you, M. Canler, do all in your power to discover the young man whose description I gave you, for it is certainly he who committed the crime of which I am suspected."

"Be at your ease, sir," I said to him. "I had already a grave reason to seek the culprit, in the enormity of the crime; but now a second consideration will urge me to neglect no opportunity of bringing him under the hand of justice."

Then I left him, after again assuring him that I would set every spring in motion, and that if the murderer were not arrested, it would be through no want of good-will on my part.

I rejoined my friend, to whom I told this scene. My heart was almost broken by this poor man's desperation, and I most fully shared the indignation which such a frightful accusation had aroused in him.

"I feel inclined," I said to my friend, "to go and examine the diligence way-bills."

"What is the good of that," he replied, "since it has been done several times already?"

"I do not think that it will be time thrown away," I remarked; "and for this reason; the report which my chief sent to the prefect states that the investigation of the way-bills has not led to the discovery of this Pagès or Magnès. It was supposed that all was done that could be in this quarter; but I do not arrive at that conclusion, for the reason that this young man of Toulouse, on coming to Paris, had never seen Madame Sénépart. I conclude from this that he did not premeditate the crime which he committed. Moreover, a man cannot make so long a journey without conversing with some of the other travellers; hence the way-bills should have been examined, not only for the day stated by M. Sénépart, but also those for the day before and the day after, through fear of an error in the date. After that, the names of all persons who came from Toulouse to Paris should have been taken down, in order to find them again by examining the guards and luggage porters. Once these travellers were discovered, they ought to have been questioned about the suspected man by the aid of his description, and in this way it would have been found out whether, during the course of conversation, anything transpired that might make known the purpose of his coming to Paris."

We proceeded to the Messageries Royales, in the Rue Montmartre, but the way-bills did not contain the name of any passenger coming from Toulouse. Then I went to Laffitte's and Caillard's, where the names of Pagès and Magnès were not to be found; but I noticed that of Graves, followed by the qualification, Colonel of Artillery, and stated to have come from Toulouse. I at once stuck to this name, for the following reason: the victim's brother-in-law, as I have already stated, had served in the artillery, and now resided at Toulouse. I thought it possible that this M. Graves might know the ex-officer, and he might be able to give me some information about the murderer. I therefore set out in search of the colonel, whom I found after considerable trouble.

"Colonel," I said to him, after explaining who I was, "do you know the Sénéparts at Toulouse?"

"I have that honour, sir."

"You are probably aware of the tragical event which has just thrown it into mourning?"

"I have this moment read it in the *Gazette des Tribunaux.*" And as he said this, the colonel showed me the paper lying before him.

"Permit me, in that case, colonel, to ask you a few questions."

"Do so, sir; I am quite ready to answer."

After telling him of the circumstances that followed the discovery of the crime, the depositions and suspicions of the victim's son, and, lastly, the description of the suspected person, I asked him whether he could remember having seen among the young people who visited the Toulouse Sénéparts, an individual bearing any resemblance to the one whom I had just described.

"I have a confused idea," he replied, "of having seen a young man to whom the description you have just given me might apply; but it is only a vague, uncertain reminiscence, and I could not make any positive assertion."

I thanked him for his kindness, and left; but I had scarce reached the foot of the stairs when an idea occurred to me. I went up again, and at once asked him whether he knew of any one in Paris who was on friendly terms with this sorely used family.

"Yes," he said; "a Madame Gibou, who lives in the Rue d'Orléans."

"Which one? there are three streets of that name."

"Ah! that I cannot tell you, or the number either."

Off I set for the Rue d'Orléans St. Honoré, going from house to house to ask.

"Madame Gibou?"

"What is she?"

"I don't know."

"It isn't here."

Vexed, but not discouraged, I left the commercial quarter for the quieter abodes of the Marais, and there I at length found the person whom I was seeking, on a fifth floor. Here came a new introduction, and the details already given to M. Graves; then I asked Widow Gibou whether the person whom I described to her had brought her any message from the Toulouse Sénéparts?

"Yes, sir, on Wednesday, the 4th, a young man came here, perfectly resembling the portrait you have drawn, who brought me letters from the young ladies; he also asked my permission to call again, but I know neither his name nor address."

"Well, madame, that young man is Madame Séné-part's murderer."

I really thought that the old lady was going to faint.

"Is it possible?"

"Yes, madame; and I venture to hope that you will give me your assistance in capturing the wretch."

"Only tell me what I am to do, sir, and be assured

that I shall do all in my power to help you, under the circumstances."

"It will be a very easy matter. The young man asked leave to call on you again, and he will return, for he knows very well that his victim was unable to speak, and he believes himself perfectly in safety. When he presents himself, receive him as you did the first time, that is to say, like a friend of the family. Let him in no way suspect that you know him to be the murderer; then, without any trouble or affectation, merely open your window. At that signal, the agents whom I shall place day and night before your house, will hurry up and effect the arrest."

On the day after, the assassin called on Madame Gibou, and was arrested. He was at once brought to my office; he was a lad of one-and-twenty, short, thin, beardless, with an effeminate face, rendered even more effeminate by long light hair; he stated that his name was Ducroc, and he was the son of a cutler at Toulouse. I took him before the magistrate, where he was confronted with M. Sénépart, who, on seeing him, exclaimed, "That is my mother's assassin! it was he who called on me, and he committed the crime!" Then turning to me, he threw his arms round my neck, and said, in tears, "Ah, Monsieur Canler, what an immense service you have rendered me! I can no longer be suspected of having assassinated my mother!"

Ducroc confessed that he committed the crime solely to buy clothes and amuse himself at public dancing-rooms with women. When sentenced to death, he displayed great penitence, and, overcome by his remorse, he ascended the scaffold with resignation.

CHAPTER XIV.

A WATCH ROBBERY.

THE most ordinary event has always a cause: and in order to discover that cause, the smallest peculiarities that have preceded the effect produced must not be neglected; and probable motives and possible reasonings must be analysed to arrive at the truth by induction. It is by practising this system that I succeeded in arresting a great number of malefactors, and, among others, those connected with the following affair.

A burglary was committed at night in the shop of a watchmaker in the Rue St. Denis. The robbers entered the shop by breaking open a side door in the passage. They seized a number of gold and silver watches hanging in the window, and then went off, leaving behind them a wooden-handled chisel, which they had employed in bursting the lock, and a candle-end, wrapped in a piece of paper about half the size of a hand.

M. S—— did not discover the robbery till he came down to his shop in the morning; and I was not informed of the daring burglary till ten o'clock. I at once proceeded with an agent to the shop, in order to collect any indications that might help me to discover the robbers; but there was not the slightest clue. No one had seen them, and, excepting the two articles to which I have referred, no object of a nature to facilitate a search was left in the shop. Under these circumstances I resolved to call on the police commissioner of the quarter, who might, perhaps, possess more precise data; but this magistrate told me that nothing could be done for the present, and that it would be wise to keep quiet for a while, as any steps could only lead to loss of time and useless labour. Then the conversation changed, and while talking of one thing and the other, I mechanically took up the piece of paper, which was three inches long at the most, that surrounded the candle-end. All at once my eyes were dazzled, as if by a sunbeam. I had read, beneath the dirty finger-marks, the four words, "Two pounds of butter," written in an illegible manner, and with an ink whose paleness rendered them even more difficult to decipher.

"By Jove!" I exclaimed, "that is a prodigious accident. I must find out the person who wrote those words, and then, perhaps, I shall get a clue to my thieves."

"My dear fellow," the commissioner said, with a

laugh, "I have known many castles-in-the-air built, but up to the present not one of them has seemed to me so improbable, and, I might almost say, so impossible, as yours."

"Perhaps so, perhaps so; who knows whether I may not succeed? But for that purpose you must lend me this piece of paper."

"Oh, willingly! Still I warn you that I mean to close the report at four o'clock, and send all these articles to the prefecture."

"Very good; I will make haste."

"Well, then, here's luck to you!"

And I went off, accompanied by an agent, and holding the small piece of paper.

I jumped into a cab and visited unsuccessfully all the markets in turn. Disappointed, I was returning to the commissioner's office, when I noticed, in the Rue Aubrey le Boucher, a butter dealer, to whom I handed my bit of paper, while repeating my usual formula. After turning it over and over, the dealer said, "Why, I wrote those words; but I don't know to whom they were addressed. It is a ticket which I stuck on two pounds of butter, sold to some passer-by or customer." On hearing this, I fell back from the seventh heaven to earth and went off.

As I walked along I said to myself that the robbery was performed either at the beginning of the night, that is to say, at one in the morning, or the burglars waited till a later hour. But the latter theory was inadmissible, because at a later hour the Rue St. Denis is filled with carts going to market and artisans proceeding to work. Hence the robbery was committed *at about one in the morning.* If this was the case, the robbers, in order not to arouse the suspicion of persons dwelling in the same house as themselves, did not go home to bed: they probably spent the night in some low wine vaults, the Courtelle for instance, and that would explain how, in going down the Faubourg du Temple, they purchased the candle in that quarter. While discussing the circumstances which must have preceded the robbery, I turned into the Rue du Faubourg du Temple, where I went from chandler's shop to chandler's shop, asking whether anyone recognised my bit of paper—it was the lantern with which Diogenes sought a man. At length I came to No. 62, near the barracks, and to my great satisfaction the following answer was returned to my question:

"Yes, sir; at about half after eleven last night I sold a halfpenny candle, wrapped in the paper you now show me, to two young men who live in the next house."

"What is their trade?"

"Ah, sir, they are as quiet as lambs! They are commercial travellers, and both out of work just at present. They smuggle laces from Belgium, but they are as well-behaved as girls; they see nobody; they frequent no bad company; they do not drink or quarrel."

I thanked my chandler for his information, and said that it was not with these young men that I had anything to do. But as I feared lest he might warn the robbers, or give them the alarm by his chattering, I sent my agent to fetch one of his comrades. During the interval I made the neighbours talk, and obtained a description of the malefactors. On the arrival of the inspectors I set them to watch, with orders to arrest the robbers if they went out, and at four o'clock the next morning I went up and arrested them. I could see nothing of a suspicious nature in their room. I sent for the commissioner, but a search led to no result, and I began to fear, not that I was mistaken, but that I had arrived too late and that the watches had fled. There was in the room a large window looking out into the yard, which I opened to let in some fresh air, and as I leant out I perceived a blacksmith's shop.

"By Jove!" I said to myself, "it would not be so very extraordinary if that smith made the chisel, without knowing to what use it would be turned." So, taking the instrument, which had been brought, I went down to the forge and asked the master whether the tool were of his making.

"No, sir," he answered me; "but I put it in a handle for one of the young men with whom you now are. He said he wanted to use it for opening cases."

There was no further doubt, and these were the burglars; hence I hurried up again, and the search began more strictly than before. The mattresses were ripped open, the paillasse gutted, the walls sounded, the boards taken up, and every hole and corner inspected. We were in despair, for we could find nothing, and after three-quarters of an hour of useless searching we resolved to go away. But the next morning I commenced a fresh search in their room, and on examining the ceiling, I noticed an almost imperceptible difference of colour, over the bed. I jumped on to a chair, and a vigorous blow of my fist on the spot produced a hole, from which tumbled pell-mell on to the bed gold and silver watches, all stolen from M. S——. Our two rogues, in order to hide the stolen articles, had made a hole in the ceiling, which they covered again with thick paper and whitewashed over, and it only appeared of a darker colour because it was not quite dry yet.

Some time after, the two burglars were tried at the assizes, and sentenced to ten years' penal servitude; and yet on what did the success of this affair depend? Upon a piece of paper to which no one had paid any attention!

CHAPTER XV.

AN ESCAPE FROM PRISON.

THE resolution of a prisoner who wishes to escape is very curious ; it is especially an astounding thing to witness the energy, the prudence, the sagacity, and constancy which a man requires to attack the mass of stone that surrounds him like a winding-sheet, and the lumps of iron which, in the shape of chains, locks, bolts and bars, separate him from society, sunshine, and liberty. But if the heart sympathizes with the escape of a Latude, for instance, who attacks with a single nail the thick walls of the Bastille, and who after years of trouble and toil has just prepared his escape, and, discovered, begins afresh the great work of deliverance, it is not the same on hearing the news of the escape of a dangerous robber or formidable assassin. All honest people are in such a case affected by terror, for liberty for the escaped convict is a prospect that a new crime will shortly horrify the public.

On August 3rd, 1843, fifteen prisoners, detained for crimes of a more or less serious nature, escaped from La Force by a tunnel, which they dug with knives and pieces of iron, in the cesspool, which had just been emptied. This extraordinary task, executed simultaneously by the fifteen prisoners, was intended to pass under the prison-wall and terminate at the baths facing the Rue Culture-Sainte Catherine; but instead of the passage opening by the side of the house, it ran into a bath-room. The malefactors, who expected to get out into the gardens, here found an obstacle on which they had not calculated, and were obliged to upheave the flooring boards with their backs. This escape, executed with so much perseverance and with such admirable secrecy, did not turn out happily for all who attempted it. An alarm was given by a person employed in the baths, and the majority were at once arrested by the inhabitants of the adjacent houses, though not without danger for those brave citizens; for the prisoners, seeing their labour thrown away and their plans of escape foiled, became furious and tried to force a passage with their knives. Only three succeeded in escaping, among these being the soul of the plot, Jean Courteau, a man of rare energy, exceptional strength, and unparalleled boldness.

Several days elapsed before the police could find the slightest trace of the fugitives. One morning my chief sent for me, and told me it was most injurious to our staff that we had not arrested at least one of these malefactors. "We shall lose our reputation," he added, "so pray do your best."

Courteau had lived for a long time in the Rue Sainte

Marguerite, Saint Antoine, where he was perfectly well known. I thought that, after his escape, he would ere long go and pay a visit to his old friends; but there was not much hope of obtaining the slightest information from any of the inhabitants, for Courteau inspired such terror that no one would have liked to aid, whether directly or indirectly, in his arrest, through fear of invoking his vengeance or that of his criminal companions, with whom the lodging-houses in the Rue Sainte Marguerite were thronged at that time.

I knew a young man of sixteen or seventeen years of age, who lived in the vicinity, and who had on several occasions rendered the police some slight services, though no one suspected his co-operation. I sent for him to come and see me at my house, at seven in the morning. He kept the appointment, and answered in the affirmative when I asked him whether he knew Courteau.

"Are you willing," I asked him, "to do me a service which I shall not forget?"

"Certainly, M. Canler. What is it that you wish me to do?"

"Something very easy; the first time you see Courteau, you will follow him closely to know where he goes, and come at once to warn me, at my own house, if at night, or at the office, from eight in the morning till ten at night. Is that settled?"

"You can depend on me."

Three days after, he came at ten o'clock at night to the prefecture to tell me that he had seen Courteau leave the Rue St. Marguerite, accompanied by two of his comrades, to whom he showed a knife, saying, "This is to kill the first agent who attempts to arrest me!" He added, that the three men were at this moment at Père Martin's liquor-shop at the Barrière de Montreuil. I resolved at once to take advantage of this information; and at half-past ten got into a fiacre, with two agents and my young informer, to go to the barrier; but halfway up the street of the same name we met Courteau returning with his two comrades. To attempt arresting him at once would have been madness; for, in consequence of the energy which I knew he possessed, he must be seized unawares, so that he could not use his knife. On the other hand, if we all four got out of the cab in this deserted street, it would afford him time for flight in the opposite direction.

I at once formed my plan, for I felt certain of the co-operation of one of my agents, of the name of Laporte, who was young, short, quick, and active, and endowed with courage and intelligence. I let the coachman drive on, and when I considered that the vehicle was so far off that Courteau could no longer hear the sound of the wheels, I bade the driver turn round, and go at full speed to the Rue St. Antoine. I thought that by this trick our robber would be far from suspecting that our coach was the one which had just passed him.

"You," I said to my agent, "will hold the right-hand door open, so that the jolting may not make it rattle. I will do the same with the other door, and when we arrive opposite our game we will jump out without stopping the fiacre, so as to have on our side all the advantage of a surprise."

The fiacre turned round, and went at the full speed of which a hackney-coach is capable. When opposite our man I leapt out, Laporte followed me, and the shock I received in jumping was so great, that I cannoned like a billiard-ball against Courteau, who was fortunately just in the position to prevent me dashing my brains out against the opposite wall. Laporte, who had a narrow escape of breaking legs and arms, caught hold of our robber, and we all three rolled in the gutter. Never was an arrest effected in such an unexpected manner or with so much promptness.

We got up, but each still held hold of Courteau's arms, and we thus led him to the Montreuil guard-house; while our fiacre proceeded to Paris, and the robber's companions ran off at full speed in a salutary state of terror.

On Courteau was found the knife to which I have already referred. On the next day he was conveyed to the depôt of the prefecture, and thence back to La Force.

CHAPTER XVI.

THE CATAIGNE MURDER.

At about four in the morning of April 3rd, 1842, some quarrymen were going down into a plaster-quarry near Chaumont, to begin work, when they discovered the corpse of a man, about fifty years of age, whose dress, though not fashionable, displayed a certain amount of care. A ribbon of the Legion of Honour, fastened in the button-hole of his black cloth coat, might have led to a belief in an accident or a suicide; but the face and body covered with wounds made with a sharp instrument, clearly proved that a murder had taken place. The body was conveyed to the Morgue, and soon recognised as that of a Sieur Cataigne, a driver in the service of one M. Julian, livery-stable keeper in the Rue St. Dominique, Saint Germain.

Cataigne had a daughter about six-and-twenty years of age, a shoe-binder by trade, residing in the Rue Saint Merri. She knew that her father had pledged a gold chain and key in the Rue Dauphin, and always carried the ticket in his pocket-book. So soon as she heard of her father's murder, she had the rare presence of mind to go to the commissioner who managed this branch office, to request him to have any person arrested who offered to redeem the pledge.

The police made useless efforts to discover the perpetrator or perpetrators of this crime. They had no sign, no information which could guide them in this dark affair, when a man of the name of Muller, a journeyman tinman, of Russian origin, a stout, stupid fellow, went to the pawn office in the Rue Dauphin, to redeem the pledged articles. He expressed himself with great difficulty, and it needed great politeness to discover French in his jargon.

In conformity with the desire expressed by the victim's daughter, the presenter of the ticket was detained, and the police commissioner was fetched to arrest him.

Muller declared that the ticket was sold him at nine o'clock on the previous evening for two francs, twenty-five cents., by three persons whom he did not know, but who were seated with him at the same table in a wine-shop of the Courtille. He passed the night in the depôt, and the next morning was handed over to me to help me in my search, and describe, were it possible, the persons who sold him the ticket. I therefore set out with this man and three agents to explore the liquor-shops of the Courtille. While passing across the Place de Grève, I noticed a street-walker of the lowest class, a prowler about the barrier, and thief, when opportunity served, who had just been arrested for an assault.

On reaching the Courtille, I visited all the dram-shops, but in vain. At about seven in the evening, the agents and Muller, who had been walking about since mid-day without resting, expressed a desire for a little rest and food; for this purpose we entered a public-house, where I ordered the traditional lump of veal and salad, only to be procured at the suburban refreshment-houses. While waiting for the food, I employed the time in asking some questions of my informer, and among others the following :—

"Did you not see one or more women with the men who sold you the ticket?"

"Yes," he answered, in his almost unintelligible jargon; "I saw the one whom the police were taking across the Place de Grêve this morning as we passed."

I gently upbraided him for not having told me this circumstance before, and leaving the Russian and my agents to swallow their dinner, I jumped into a cab and hastened to the prefecture, when I ordered the girl in question to be brought to me.

Her name was Annette Lenoir, and she appeared very savage at her arrest, hence she made no difficulty about answering me.

"Were you not," I asked her, "at a wine-shop in the Courtille last Saturday night?"

"Yes, sir."

"Whom were you with?"

"Three men, whose names I do not know, excepting one who has the nickname of Delicate."

"Give me as exact a description as you can of this man and his comrades."

She obeyed.

"Now tell me, did you not see one of these men sell some pawn-tickets?"

"Sell? no, sir; but I saw Delicate with such on his hand, and showing them to his companions. He had also a large coloured paper to which there was a seal, and I thought it was a discharge, because the man who looked at it said, 'Well, you are all right with that, at any rate.'"

I left the girl, with a promise to have her set at liberty, if the information she had given me proved correct. I returned to the Courtille to examine the drinking-houses, and at midnight entered the lodging-house kept by Father Joseph, in the Passage Philibert. I asked whether he had as lodger a man whose description I gave him, and whom his comrades had christened Delicate.

"I believe I have your man," he answered me; "there is a lad here with that nickname, but he has not come in yet."

"Has he any companions in your house?"

"Yes; an intimate friend, called Big Charles, who is also out at present."

I asked for a description of the latter, and it tallied very closely with that given by the girl. I at once installed two agents in the house with orders not to let the keeper out of sight, for I feared an indiscretion on his part, which would not have been at all extraordinary, and is general at thieves' lodging-houses. I kept the other agent with me, and we watched the approaches to the house; but the two men did not return all night. At nine in the morning Big Charles came up and was arrested, as was Delicate during the course of the day.

The inquiry showed that Big Charles was one Joseph Mirault, twenty-nine years of age, native of Blois, and journeyman saddler by trade. The name of Delicate was Victor Vallée, born at Sens, twenty-four years of age, and labourer on the quays. They were both condemned to death; the first was executed, while the punishment of the second was commuted to penal servitude for life. As for the third accomplice, Edward Villetard, more cunning than his comrades, on the very day after the murder he entered the Hôpital du Midi as a patient, in the hope of establishing an *alibi*; but for all that he was condemned to twenty years' penal servitude.

These three villains belonged to that infamous class of which Eugène Sue has given us a very exact type in his "Mysteries of Paris."

CHAPTER XVII.

I AM APPOINTED PEACE-OFFICER.

Toward the close of 1842, I was ordered to assist M. Eloin, the police commissioner to the judicial commission, in arresting Vidocq, who, after being robber, convict, and detective, was now keeping an office, or rather was carrying on an opposition police. It was the third time since 1833 that I had been instructed to lock him up in the depôt of the prefecture. During the operation I expressed my desire to be appointed a peace-officer.

"Why so?" M. Eloin asked me; "surely you are comfortable in the detective branch?"

"That is true, but periods succeed and do not resemble each other. From 1832 to 1839, my relations with my chief were always most agreeable; but since agent B—— has succeeded in persuading him that the activity which I display is only intended to overthrow him and take his place, I have endured considerable annoyance, to which I should like to put an end so soon as possible."

And the conversation broke off here. But on

January 1, 1844, M. Eloin, on being appointed head of the municipal police, remembered my wishes; he spoke to the secretary-general, and both promised me promotion upon the first vacancy. On September 1, 1844, I was really appointed in the place of the peace-officer of the 6th arrondissement, and inspector of the theatres of the Boulevard du Temple, who retired on his pension. The next day the secretary-general took me to the prefect's office, when I took the oath. On this occasion M. Delessert made a paternal address about the new duties I was about to fulfil, and added —"I have often been informed of the important services you have rendered my department, I therefore hope you will not forget that you once belonged to the detective force, and that your duties as municipal policeman will not prevent you from watching and arresting criminals in your district."

As may be supposed, I did not hesitate to join this plan, and I was no sooner installed, than I began reflecting seriously about the promise I had made the prefect, and the difficulties which I should have to overcome.

In fact, what is the soul of the policeman? Money: for he must have in his pay, first, skilful, active and intelligent agents by profession, who second their chief in his plans and wishes, accomplish his orders, follow his plans, in a word, realize the thought which he has conceived; and, secondly, denouncers, contemptible beings, dragged out of crime by fear, and selling to the police, for a small fee, the secrets of their comrades.

Next, what are the means given to the head of the detective department to simplify, facilitate, and foster his operations? The centralization of information which tells him every day what crimes have been committed, what convicts have broken their bans, what malefactors have entered the lodging-houses, and a thousand other not merely useful but indispensable facts and occurrences.

Now, I had not at my disposal one halfpenny of the 31,200 francs allotted at that period to the detective force annually, to pay informers and stimulate the zeal of the agents. I was alone, without resources, information, or a single member of the profession to facilitate the execution of the task which I had taken on myself. I must therefore seek auxiliaries sufficiently disinterested to serve me gratuitously; but as perfect disinterestedness is very rare, I sought among the individuals whom I had to watch those who might usefully serve me as informers and allies. I thought that I could only find such among the mistresses and girls in the tolerated houses, the keepers of thieves' lodgings, the sellers of checks at the doors of theatres, and lastly, the street-sellers, who often possess precious information. Instead of attaching myself to one class, I took them all into my service in the following way.

Street-walkers are frequently arrested for trifles, which it is, however, necessary to repress, in order to keep under a yoke of iron these degraded creatures, who are prone to licence. After referring the matter to the head of the municipal police, I paid a visit to the mistresses of tolerated houses in my district. I promised them my protection when in trouble, on condition that if robbers visited them, or they learned from their girls any peculiar facts connected with malefactors, they would at once let me know.

This point settled, I turned my attention to the keepers of the thieves' lodging-houses, and all promised to keep me well posted up. Still most of these men did not keep their promises, and as I had my own way of compelling them, I put it in execution. I went, at all hours of the night, with the police commissioner, to make a search in their houses, and arrested every lodger whose papers were not perfectly in order or who had none. At times, too, I went with my policemen to their houses at three or four in the morning and made all the lodgers get up and dress, under pretext of seeking a criminal who was not there. The keepers of these houses soon saw that their customers, annoyed by such continued disturbances, gradually decreased, and that they would have ere long only empty rooms to show me. My surveillance did not appear likely to cease soon, and they at length understood that it would be better to compound with me than go on struggling so disadvantageously: they did of compulsion what the women had done freely, and all was for the best in this quarter.

I had next to make sure of the sellers of theatrical checks. They were not very difficult to reduce. A surveillance at the doors of the theatres led to the arrest of any committing an offence, and they were sure to be sent to prison the next morning. Such were the means that subjugated them and rendered them my devoted slaves.

In the fourth place, I made allies of the street-sellers, who hawk without a licence articles which they sell at a cheap rate and have bought at a still lower rate. With these I employed the same system which had succeeded so capitally with the women, and by tolerating their standing at the corners of passages and at certain places in the streets, I obtained from them valuable information which their nomadic life enabled them to pick up.

All this arranged, I obtained fresh allies by attaching exclusively to my service informers whom I selected among liberated convicts, forbidden to dwell in the capital, and whom I arrested for infraction of that prohibition. I noticed among them several gifted with rare intelligence, and I obtained for them a temporary leave to remain in Paris.

One of these men, Charles R——, who had been already twice sentenced, and had now broken his ban, was wonderfully clever; he possessed such an extraordinary memory and glance that he recognised immediately and without hesitation any man with whom he had been in prison, and whom he might not have seen for years. If this person tried to conceal himself under a false name, Charles at once said to him—

"That is not your name; you are so-and-so; at such a time you were in such a room of such a prison."

With such qualities he could not fail to render me important services. Unhappily I had to pay for his support, and that of my other informers, to prevent them relapsing into their old evil habits, and, as I said, there was no money at my disposal till I hit on the following plan. Each day I gave these men some theatrical orders out of the heap sent at that time to the police commissioners. These orders, sold for fifty centimes to persons who wished to enter without waiting their turn, secured each of my men some three or four francs a day. This sale insured a modest livelihood, and allowed them to devote all their time to me.

After making these preliminary arrangements, I selected among the sixteen policemen, two, Sallier and Toisoul, in whom I had entire confidence; and I never met two men more devoted to their duty. It was thus that I succeeded in making a staff of skilful, clever, indefatigable allies, who rendered me the greatest services and immensely facilitated the success of my operations. Owing to their help I was enabled to hunt down all the criminals in my district, and the following was my first affair.

A few days after my installation, a young lawyer's clerk from the country, newly arrived in Paris, was attacked about midnight in the Rue du Haut Moulin by four men, who gagged him, and stole his watch, purse, hat, and pocket-knife. For three weeks the detectives had been making useless researches, and the affair would probably have been let drop, had not a ticket-taker at a theatre, who lived in the same house as the clerk, advised him to come to me, saying, "Go to the peace-officer, tell him what has happened to you, and if he does not find your robbers, no one will find them." The young provincial called on me and told me all the details of this nocturnal attack, and gave me a description, as well as he could, of the four men. "What most annoys me is," he added, "that at the prefecture they told me they did not believe my story; and yet, sir, I swear to you that it is exactly true."

Persuaded that the young man spoke the truth, I sent him away, promising to make active inquiries, and warn him if I got hold of the robbers. "Hang it!" I could not refrain from saying to myself when he had gone, "this is a ticklish affair; the detectives have given it up, and it would be a famous beginning if I succeeded."

The next dayI set out on my task with my two picked agents, and one of my spies, who in the revolution of 1848 enlisted in the Garde Mobile, and was killed by the insurgents at the barricade of the Faubourg du Temple. After three days' incessant search, we at length captured the four robbers, and found on one of them the clasp-knife and the ticket of the watch, which he had pawned. The prefect, on being informed of the result, sent to congratulate me.

Another robbery, which also had its importance, though it belonged to a very different class, soon succeeded this one. One of our street-selling allies informed us that he had heard how three young men, of whom he gave the description, had, on the previous evening, plundered a man, whom they had previously stupified with a narcotic and then carried home like a dead man.

It was eight in the morning when I received this revelation, and I at once sent off the two agents and R—— to visit all the drinking-shops in the Faubourg du Temple and at Belleville, which are generally much frequented by thieves, and by eleven o'clock the three robbers were arrested. I cross-questioned the youngest, a beardless lad of seventeen, who at the first word I spoke began crying. I took advantage of his feelings to talk about his father and mother, made him notice the dangerous position he was in, and the pain he would cause his parents. I allowed him to see that by perfect frankness he might perhaps get out of the scrape; and then I added by way of peroration, "Whether you speak or not, the affair will still go on, for within an hour I shall know in what house the robbery was committed, and you will be confronted with your victim; but in that case do not reckon upon my indulgence, for I shall be pitiless to you." At these words be fell on his knees, swearing through his sobs that he would confess everything, and said to me—

"At eleven o'clock last night my two comrades and I were on the Place du Châtelet, when we saw a man coming toward us so drunk that he could hardly stand. 'Hilloa!' said the eldest of us three, 'there is a man of whom there is something to make. Follow me!' He accosted the drunkard, got into conversation with him, and took him without difficulty to a wine-shop, where we were soon seated over a bottle. My comrade, the one who had hitherto spoken, put some tobacco in his mouth, chewed it, and while we were talking with our chance friend, squeezed the quid into his glass. At midnight we left; the poor man could not stand, so we carried him to his room in the Rue St. Denis, at a house where there is no porter. After undressing and putting our drunkard to bed, we left him and took the key with us. At one o'clock we returned, and found our man fast asleep. We made a bundle of his clothes; took his money, and then went off. That is the exact truth, sir. I know perfectly well that I have acted very wrong, but I am not a thief. I was obliged to behave like my two companions, or they would have beaten me."

After this revelation, I went with my two agents to the house in the Rue St. Denis, where we found the robbed man still in bed, and unsuspicious of what had occurred. Greatly surprised at what we told him, he jumped out of bed, upset the mattresses, and, then, surveying a pocket-book that lay between them, he uttered an indescribable cry of joy as he said, "Ah, gentlemen, how glad I am at having escaped so cheaply! If my robbers had thought of searching between the mattresses, I should have been ruined, for this pocket-book contains 80,000 francs which I received the day before yesterday. But I intend to place them in safety this very day."

The man confirmed, as far as his memory served, a portion of the details derived from the youthful thief, and he hastily accompanied us to the police commissioner, who sent the three young scamps to the prefecture.

At the same period, a request which I was far from anticipating, led me to turn my attention to another robbery. M. Allard had a brother who was a sergent de ville, and whose wife kept an eating-house. Two robbers got into her shop and stole a canvas bag, containing 1200 francs in five franc pieces. The head of the detective branch was at once informed of this by his brother, and as the robbers were known, the only thing now was to get hold of them ; but as M. Allard had been unable to effect the arrest, he resolved to ask me to arrest these two men should I happen to discover them.

I took the field, accompanied by my corporal, my two agents, and several allies. I visited all the ill-famed resorts in the district, and it was lucky that I did so, for at half-past ten the next night I arrested the two malefactors at a liquor-shop in the Rue des Fossés du Temple, frequented by most of the scamps from the boulevard. At the moment of arrest, one of the robbers, a veteran in crime, dashed at me with a clasp-knife to stab me, and I certainly should not have escaped the blow he tried to deal me, had it not been for the presence of mind and coolness of my corporal, who clutched the scoundrel's arm, and thus enabled me to disarm him. A search made at the lodgings of the robbers led to the discovery of the canvas bag which had once contained the 1200 francs, but there was not a farthing in it now.

This affair was only just terminated when I met on the boulevard an agent in the detective service, who told me, among other things, that the police, for three weeks past, had been wanting a man of the name of Schneider and two of his comrades, who were professional thieves, and warrants were out against them.

"I fancy," the agent added, "that they will never be found, for they know they are pursued, and are too artful to let themselves be taken."

"The future will teach us that," I thought; and on returning to my office I told my confidants what the detective had told me. Two or three days had hardly elapsed ere one of my allies, belonging to the class of street-sellers, informed me that the persons wanted were in hiding in a room situated on the fifth story of a house in the Rue de Lourcine, and that they never went out by day, but worked at night. At four o'clock the next morning, Schneider and his two accomplices were arrested, and, by order, the detective department handed me the warrants which they held, and had been unable to set in use.

I will not describe here my various operations during the five years I did duty as peace officer. I will confine myself to stating that I handed over to justice criminals of every description. Hence, M. Eloin congratulated me frequently, and was fond of saying that I was the first peace officer who had ever been a detective as well. I was destined to be the only one, for my successors confined themselves to their municipal duties.

I will terminate this chapter with an affair which was rather curious, owing to its tragical ending. It was in December, 1844, and people frequently complained of robberies committed in the theatres, especially in the dress-circles. During the performances on two consecutive Sundays, an overcoat had been stolen at the Folies Dramatiques and another at the Delassements Comiques. I obtained from the box-openers a description of the person whom they suspected to be the thief, and foreseeing that the clever rogue would continue his performances on the next Sunday, I placed an agent at the money-taker's box of every theatre, except the Gaîté, which I reserved for myself. Each agent had a description of the individual, as well as orders to follow him when he came, and only to arrest him in the act.

In order to adhere to this plan of action I stationed myself behind the little wooden bar that divides the pay-office, whence I could see everybody without being seen myself. The first act of the *Seven Castles of the Demon* passed, and my man did not appear. I thought that he might possibly be at some other theatre, but as the bell rang for the second act I saw a man come in whom I at once recognised as a liberated convict—one Joseph Martin, formerly a professor of mathematics. He had a ticket for the dress circle. I immediately gave my secretary a sign to remain on the watch in the lobby, and then went to my box, whence I could observe all the fellow's movements. At the end of the second act I saw him raise his arm, lower it, put it to his pocket, and then leave the box, and I at once left my own, and ran to seize his hands, so that he might not make away with the stolen article. I took him to the police office, where he was searched, and in the pocket of his overcoat was found the gold eye-glass of the lady who had been seated in front of him. I had in my pocket-book the addresses of the two gentlemen who had been robbed on the previous Sundays. I sent for them, and when they arrived, one recognised his own overcoat upon the thief's back, and among the objects taken from his pocket the other gentleman found a cigar case which a week previously had been in the pocket of the coat stolen from him. In the face of such crushing evidence my thief did not attempt any denial. He confessed everything carelessly, and owing to this arrest was sentenced to fifteen months' imprisonment and surveillance.

This thief was a well-mannered man, he had enjoyed an excellent education, and expressed himself with fluency, even with elegance. A few years later, his claims became of a higher order, under the following circumstances.

The revolution of February, 1848, arrived, and our thief, under a false name and through his impudence, contrived to get appointed one of the sub-commissioners, who temporarily took the place of the under-prefect. He was sent to a rich and populous town; but a few months after entering on his duties he met in his new residence one of his old prison friends of the name of Fouqué, like himself under surveillance, and who had equally broken his ban. This convict, without any hesitation, told the new official of his state of destitution, and the representative of authority slipped a small sum of money into his hand while urging him to be silent, and he would supply his wants. For a time all went well, the sub-commissioner's ex-prison colleague was delighted at having an annuity, and living at his ease. For a while he was moderate, but with time his demands for money grew more frequent and high. The public functionary raised objections, but the other began bullying, and our ex-thief paid up at once to procure silence. The demands again increased, and refusals were followed by such menaces that Martin was forced to give what was asked of him. Still, as it was not an endurable existence to have such a sword of Damocles suspended over his head, our magistrate invited his parasite to accompany him upon a country walk. They set out, and while passing through a small wood Martin assassinated Fouqué with two pistol-shots, and as his victim still breathed, finished him with forty-one dagger-stabs.

A month after the crime the murderer was detected, and sentenced to penal servitude for life.

CHAPTER XVIII.

THE PREFECTURE OF POLICE IN 1848.

I DO not pretend here to narrate the history of the revolution of 1848, for that grand social shock has been justified or criticised by quite enough public writers. As a passionless observer, I shall confine myself to saying that, in the course of my career, circumstances enabled me to receive so many confidences, and to learn such secrets about men and things, that in political matters I have grown to be much of the opinion of the Orientals. I believe in destiny—in predestination!

Hence I will not write a political treatise: the mission I have undertaken is far more modest: I have no other object than to relate what I have seen, done, and ordered to be done.

The Reform Banquet was fixed for February 23rd, 1848, and at twelve o'clock on the previous evening I received orders to remain in my district with all my sergeants from seven in the morning, and send hourly reports to the municipal police about the popular movements and the state of public opinion.

I established my head-quarters at the police-room of

the Gaîté Theatre, and I waited there while each of my sergeants came to tell me all he had seen and heard during his round.

The Boulevards have been justly compared to an immense artery in which the population of the capital, the blood of the great city, circulates, and on them the progress of agitation may be followed step by step. I was so situated as to witness the prelude of the grand coming drama, which was fated to begin like all revolutions, with shouts, and end with the overthrow of the monarchical power and the accession of the republican government.

The Faubourgs St. Antoine and St. Marceau, which played so great a part in the Revolution of '89, seemed to be aroused. A considerable number of workmen from them passed along the Boulevard between ten and eleven in the morning, proceeding towards the Champs Elysées, which was the gathering-place of the adherents of the banquet. At about two p.m., a dozen individuals, on their return, tried to break into a gunsmith's shop on the Boulevard St. Martin, but they were compelled to retire without succeeding in their design.

Between three and four o'clock, a general officer of the National Guard came up at full gallop to inform the people collected on the boulevard that the king had changed his ministry, and formed a new cabinet more in accordance with popular opinion. On hearing this, a general cry of "Long live the King!" burst from the crowd, which seemed hitherto to have had no other intention than to make a striking demonstration, it is true, but one based on the reformist manifestations of England, attacking ministers and not the king—the instruments of power and not the principal. In a word, the crowd, satisfied with this concession, at once laid aside their anger, and like children whose caprices are satisfied and pass from crying to laughter, shouts of joy followed the previous imprecations.

At half-past nine in the evening I left the Boulevard du Temple to go to the prefecture, where it was my turn to go on night duty, and I went along the Rue St. Martin and the Place du Châtelet. Nearly everywhere I passed windows were illuminated, joy was spread over all faces, tranquillity seemed to have perfectly returned, and cries of "Long live the King!" burst from the crowd of curious persons walking along this busy street. "By Jove!" I said to myself, "we shall escape this time again, with the fright and a few broken window-panes."

On reaching the prefecture, I received orders from the head of the municipal police not to send out any rounds, but to keep the police by me till eight in the morning. The authorities were persuaded that the troops would easily disperse any disturbers of the peace on the next day.

At one in the morning the heads of the police were

comfortably asleep; I alone, with the men on duty, kept awake through that night, which was destined to be the last of the reign of Louis Philippe. I walked about the courtyard, and noticed with some anxiety that an unusual calm brooded over the town. I could not hear either that slight hum which shows that a portion of the population has not yet retired to rest, the sound of carriages which announces that the fortunate ones of this world are returning to their sumptuous residences after a night of pleasure, or the creaking of the waggons which bring, during the night, the provisions of every description which Paris will consume on the morrow. It was the silence of death, or to speak more correctly, that dead calm which, in the torrid zones, ever precedes the most furious tempests. A quarter of an hour had scarce elapsed ere this awful silence was broken by the bells of the different churches mournfully pealing the tocsin. Wishing to know exactly what was going on, I sent two of my agents in civilian dress to explore the Montmartre district; but before sending them off, I carefully asked them for their cards as police inspectors, in order that they might not be maltreated if they fell into the hands of the promoters of trouble. Two other agents went into the St. Martin quarter. One hour later the first pair came back to inform me that barricades were being built at every street corner, and that in the Rue Jean Jacques Rousseau they met several individuals dragging a truck, while others rapped at doors, broke them in, and carried off the arms of the National Guards, which they deposited in the truck.

A short time after, the two agents ordered to traverse the St. Martin quarter arrived with a young man who was carrying a bayonet, and I immediately questioned him.

"I am a wine-merchant's clerk," he answered me, "at the Barrière Montparnasse, and yesterday morning my master sent me to present a bill at the Carré St. Marceau. As I was returning home I met several friends, with whom I amused myself till midnight. Then I proceeded homewards; but on reaching the Rue Transnonain, I found myself close to a powerful barricade, when I was arrested by twenty men armed with muskets. Taking me for a police agent, they surrounded and severely questioned me, while searching me from head to foot. At last they were convinced that they were mistaken on my score, and set me at liberty. From that moment up to my arrest by your agents, I saw everywhere as I passed barricades and armed men. Lastly, too, the bayonet found in my possession belongs to a musket thrown down in the street, and I secured the weapon to defend myself in the case of an attack."

The night passed without any other incident, and at eight o'clock I asked for fresh orders. "All goes well," was the reply; "all measures are taken; you can send your people away; but tell them to mind to remain at home, so that they may be found immediately, should we require their services."

I confess that I found such a resolution and such certainty of success very curious at so critical a moment.

I left the prefecture with Sallier, my agent, to go and join my sergeants, whom I had appointed to meet at the Gaîté Theatre. I arrived without obstacle at the Rue de la Verrerie, but finding several barricades in the next street, I turned back to the Bastille, where I found a detachment of troops of the line drawn up before the guard-house. At the same moment. M. Moreau, mayor of the eighth arrondissement, came up, escorted by some national guards and citizens armed with muskets. He went up to the troops and informed them that M. Odillon Barrot had just been appointed minister; but the officers and men seemed very indifferent about the news. The citizens who followed the major shouted several times, "Long live the King!" and M. Moreau, meeting with no echo, proceeded in the direction of the Faubourg St. Antoine. At this moment, either by accident or voluntarily, a shot was fired from the barricade that closed the Rue de la Roquette. On hearing this shot, the detachment on the square believed in an attack on the part of the insurgents, and responded by a discharge which killed or wounded several persons belonging to the mayor's escort. The national guards answered this unexpected attack by several shots, and this time again there were dead and wounded; but this mistake only lasted a few minutes. When the first round was fired, I and Sallier were close to the column; my agent lay down on his stomach, to escape the bullets, but I ran off at full speed in the direction of the Contrescarpe Boulevard. I had scarce gone a hundred yards, ere I received so sharp a blow on my left thigh, that I fancied a bullet had struck me; but I continued to increase my distance. Very luckily I found a house door open; into it I hurried, and my first care was to place my hand on the wound, but I noticed no blood. The sharp pain I felt had been produced by a bullet, which had ricochetted from a wall and struck the muscles of my thigh.

In consequence of what had happened, I found it impossible to reach the Boulevard du Temple. I, therefore, resolved to return to my lodgings; but, in order to do so, I must go along the entire Faubourg St. Antoine, which bristled with barricades. Now, it would have been the height of imprudence on my part to enter the faubourg, for during the eight-and-twenty years I had been employed at the prefecture of police I had become well known to the robbers, and I need only meet one of these scoundrels to get into trouble at such moments of effervescence—a pistol is so soon fired, a man falls, he is dead, and that is all!

To avoid any unpleasant encounters, I went a long way round to go to a friend of mine, M. Bonnet, who lived in the Rue de Constantine at Belleville; but, unfortunately, he was out. Annoyed by this misadventure I returned towards Paris, reflecting and wondering which way I had better turn, when I met a M. Boulenois, whom I knew, and who, armed with a musket and sabre, could not restrain an exclamation of surprise at seeing me.

"What," he said to me, "you here at such a time! You have everything to fear: all the rogues and ruffians of the Boulevard du Temple have gone to Belleville; all the honest people are terrified at it, and, as you see, we are on our guard."

"I had come to seek shelter with a friend of mine, who resides in this street; but I had not the good luck to find him, so I am returning to Paris."

"Well, come with me. You will put on a blouse and cap, and then we will fetch my wife and child; and, as I am known, we will pass the barrier together."

Ere long I was dressed in blouse and cap, with a national guard's sabre dangling against my thigh and Boulenois' little girl in my arms, and we proceeded towards Paris. The barrier of the Trois Communes, through which we wanted to pass, was guarded by some thirty fellows armed with muskets and sabres, and among them I recognised, at the first glance, half a dozen robbers whom I had arrested under different circumstances. Either through the preoccupation of the moment, or my unusual dress, they did not seem to recognise me at once, and one of them said to me—

"Are you going into Paris?"

"Yes!"

"You cannot take your sabre with you; you must leave it here."

"That is of no consequence, as I shall return directly. I will take it back as I pass."

I had scarce uttered these words when I heard a pistol cocked behind me, and a voice, which I recognised as that of a thief, say—

"Hilloh! 'tis the police-officer from the Boulevard du Temple; he has bullied me enough in his time, he has, and so I shall now blow out his brains."

But, at the same moment, a young workman of the name of Ludovic, to whose family I had done some slight service, threw himself on the man with the pistol, tore the weapon from him, and shouted, "Monsieur Canler is a good man, and I will kill with this pistol any one who dares even to give him a scratch."

These words produced all their effect; the man who wished to kill me hurriedly fell back, and Boulenois, pale and trembling during the colloquy, regaining a little coolness, we passed the barrier and reached the canal safe and sound; but as the drawbridge was pulled up, I handed over the child to her mother, and spent the rest of the night with a friend, a sergeant-major in the national guards, who lived in the Rue Fontaine du Roi.

The next morning I proceeded to the prefecture of police, whose gates had been thrown open to the people on the previous evening. The municipal guards had been disarmed, and most of the clerks had been obliged to fly, either through secret doors or by clambering over the walls. The inhabitants of the adjoining houses afforded a refuge to many of the police, and procured them means of flight by giving them mufti. The prefecture was full of workmen and tradespeople, who were curious to enter this police asylum, which had hitherto been concealed from their gaze.

As everybody knows, Caussidière was appointed prefect of police. I willingly do him the justice of stating that under his administration not one of us was dismissed. And more than that, for a long time the police were forced to hide in order to escape certain threats of vengeance, and yet they were fully paid. Hence I do not believe that any police agent, whether head or subaltern, had cause to complain of Caussidière. It is true that it was utterly impossible for him to carry on the police system properly with the men who surrounded him; still, we must give him credit for his resistance of the constant pressure put upon him to expel "all the old satellites of the tyrant."

A fact will prove that Caussidière knew how to distinguish between the success of the old police and the new recruits. The occasion was as follows.

That excessive liberty engenders excess is an axiom which will ever be true, and the Republic soon thought it necessary to take certain precautions against one of its disobedient children — Citizen Blanqui. Blanqui lived in two rooms, on the second floor of No. 1, Rue Boucher, and in these two rooms also lived a dozen men, who acted as his body-guard.

Caussidière was perfectly well aware that for this arrest he could not reckon on his Montagnards, for these quasi-soldiers were not at all suited for a job which was contrary to their feelings. Consequently, Caussidière sent for the head of the municipal police, and told him that he wished the peace officers to undertake the operation. At this period these officers did not make their appearance at the offices of the prefecture, for their presence would have been disagreeable to the Montagnards, most of whom had been arrested by them in former times for political reasons or others. The peace officers met daily from twelve till three in the public decency office, which had a separate entrance.

On the day fixed for Blanqui's arrest we remained in this office till eleven at night. We then proceeded to the cabinet of the chief of the Municipal Police, where M. Bertoglio, the police commissioner, came to join us. We were told what we had to do, and M. Bertoglio informed us that he had examined the house in which Blanqui resided; the stairs were narrow, and in the rooms which he occupied were several men armed with muskets, abundantly supplied with cartridges, and well inclined to defend themselves in case of an attack. "I must not conceal from you, gentlemen," he added, "that this affair is most perilous, and that more than one of us may remain on the field."

At midnight, all the peace officers and Sergeant Fraudin started under the guidance of M. Bertoglio. On reaching the house in question we noticed that the windows of both the rooms were open, and there was light inside. Hence, in order not to spoil the chance, it was decided that Fraudin should go and make sure of Blanqui's presence, by pretending that he had a message to deliver to him from Citizen D——, captain of the Montagnards.

This D—— was once a seller of checks on the Boulevard du Temple, who, like so many men, cleverly taking advantage of the chances of the revolution, had installed himself in the Tuileries with a few more of the same stamp, who took possession of the palace, in the name of the French people. And these gentlemen found such a difference between their new lodging and their old shake-downs at ten centimes a night, that when it was time to turn them out a compromise had to be effected with them, and they only left the palace on condition that their company should be enrolled among the Montagnards and D—— remain their captain. But to return to our subject.

Fraudin went up the two flights and rapped: a light was struck and a man appeared in the doorway.

"Whom do you want?"

"Citizen Blanqui," Frauden answered.

"Who are you, and what do you want with him?"

"I am a friend of Captain D——, and have come from him."

At this answer, the man who opened the door fell back a step, and Fraudin was enabled to enter the first room. A few trusses of straw scattered on the ground served as a bed for half-a-dozen men who were asleep with their guns by their side; there was no furniture nor anything that would give the faintest idea of an inhabited apartment. The introducer at once continued:

"Citizen Blanqui is not here, and we do not know when he will return: still, Citizen, if you will leave your message with me ——"

"It is unnecessary, I will come again," our sergeant replied, as he took a peep into the second room, the door of which was open, to make sure that Blanqui was really not there.

Fraudin rejoined us, and the expedition was put off till the next morning at six, when we met on the Pont Neuf; but we were again unsuccessful; Blanqui had not come in, and the affair remained in *statu.*

Still there was some one whom this ill success did not satisfy. Ledru Rollin, the Minister of the Interior, who trembled at Blanqui, expressed to M. Carlier, at that time head of the police to the Ministry of the Interior, his regret that Caussidière had not effected this arrest.

"If you are anxious about it," said M. Carlier, "I will have him arrested for you, but it will cost money."

"I do not care for that," the minister replied.

Three days after, Blanqui was arrested. In this way:—

M. Carlier sent for an excessively demagogic but poor chief of a club, and said to him without further preface:

"Ah! it is you, Sir? Be good enough to sit down, and allow me to enter into matters at once. I have always thought that the only reason why you were so exalted in the opinions you profess, was because you had not a penny-piece to call your own."

"Really, sir ——"

"Pray allow me to speak without interruption, and you can answer me afterwards. We desire to arrest Blanqui; here are six thousand-franc notes, which are yours, if you agree to tell us at what spot and at what hour this arrest can be effected, as you know where he goes and what he does. You need only speak one word to earn this sum."

And the word was spoken.

M. Carlier, on telling Ledru Rollin of this greatly-desired capture, only added, "You have him, but it costs you 6000 francs."

Let us return to the prefecture of police, of which Pornin, a wooden-legged man and inveterate drunkard, was appointed governor. The scenes that took place night after night in his apartments were frightful. Such was the life of some of the Montagnards, who for a season caused the capital to tremble. But let me hasten to add, that such examples of depravity and debauchery could only be found at the prefecture of police.

The events of May 15 completely freed the prefecture of the Montagnards. M. Trouvé-Chauvil took the place of Caussidière as prefect of police, and then the sergens-de-ville, who, since February 24, had been compelled to abstain from appearing at the prefecture, resumed their duties in civilian clothing.

Caussidière, while depriving himself of their aid, had understood, however, that the streets could not be left without police agents, and had created the guardians of Paris. But, as the choice of the staff was left to the good pleasure of Citizen Pornin, it is needless to say that he did not let in any of the old sergens-de-ville.

This new corps was partly composed of right-minded Montagnards, and made up with the first comers who presented themselves under their patronage and a bottle of wine for Pornin. Among the number were also individuals of peaceful manners, who, being compelled to gain a precarious livelihood, had resigned themselves to a police life; but it was impossible, owing to the elements of which it was formed, for this new creation to reach the promised object. A man does not become a policeman as he does a soldier, by the force of events and through the chances of a ballot: for such a part natural qualities are needed, which many policemen in our day do not possess, and never will possess.

It was not enough to have created guardians of Paris; they required a rallying sign, a distinctive mark; and as it was inconvenient at the time to give each new policeman a Tyrolean hat and a blue tunic, they merely gave him a brass plate bearing the words, "Prefecture of Police," and intended to be fastened by a strap to the left arm. It was very curious to see all these representatives of authority walking gravely about the streets in blouses and caps and ragged clothes, and consequently in a condition not at all edifying for the persons subjected to their surveillance.

Months succeeded each other. June 23rd arrived, and with the burning midsummer sun were kindled the first fires of that mournful civil war. At the first symptoms of that insurrection, which changed Paris into one vast battle-field, some of the guardians under my orders deserted me and joined the insurgents. One of the latter having been killed in the Rue Ménilmon tant, one of these deserters laid the body on a litter, placed himself at the head in uniform and sabre in hand, and went through all the streets of the Faubourg du Temple, showing the corpse to the people, and shouting for vengeance.

At about nine in the evening, I was ordered to go out and reconnoitre. I passed through the Faubourg du Temple with no further difficulty than having to leap over the barricades erected on all sides; but when I tried to return to the mairie of the sixth arrondissement, to report what I had seen, I found the bridges drawn up and guarded by men armed with guns. In order not to fall into their hands, I took refuge in the house of a friend, and remained there for three days, while the cannon were roaring. Through the windows looking on the canal I had noticed among the insurgents at the barricade of the Angouleme bridge, two convicts, more obstinate than the rest, who fired at the troops each time that they passed the end of the street. These two villains seemed desirous to avenge on the blood of the citizens the proscription to which society had sentenced them for their crimes. On the 21st, the day when the Faubourg du Temple was taken by the troops, I met one of these bandits, and though he was surrounded by a dozen vagabonds like himself, I did not hesitate to collar him. At a later date he was brought before the council of war, and sentenced to transportation.

Hardly was the insurrection suppressed, than from all sides poured in denunciations that so-and-so and so-and-so had taken a more or less active part in the revolt. M. Monin-Jappy, mayor of the 6th arrondissement, thought that all these denunciations could not be true, and to avoid any fatal error he ordered me to make inquiries about every person denounced. To facilitate my task, he placed a room at my service, in which I installed myself with my old policemen and the guardians who had remained faithful. I at once set to work, and I am bound to say that three-fourths of the denunciatory sentences were only dictated by the lowest and most infamous calumny, and roused by envy or private revenge.

CHAPTER XIX.

I AM APPOINTED CHIEF DETECTIVE.

IMMEDIATELY after his election, the President of the Republic appointed as Prefect of Police M. Rebillot, an ex-colonel of gendarmerie; and M. Carlier was nominated head of the Municipal Police, an office he had before held from 1831 to 1833. Owing to these two appointments, important changes took place on the staff of the prefecture. M. Allard, among others, chief of the detective staff, was allowed to retire on a pension.

M. Carlier, who had seen me at work, and who was aware that I had had long practice in police matters, thought that I might be employed with advantage at the head of the detective staff. On the 3rd of March I received my appointment, and so soon as I was installed I set actively to work in establishing new regulations and remedying various abuses.

Thus, the system of informing was not at all satisfactory, and had no regulation but the good pleasure of the denouncer, who was at times impelled to assume this character through the caprices of a jealous temper.

I resolved to organize a brigade of informers, whom I called my irregular Cossacks; for this purpose I enlisted new convicts, and subjected them to regular discipline. Each of them received high pay, for the pecuniary retribution I gave my Cossacks, by preserving them from want, was intended to prevent them from seeking means of existence in crimes, and by thus binding them to the police make them afraid of falling into their clutches again.

They were expected to do the "depôt" and the "St. John." At four o'clock every afternoon, the detectives pay a visit to the prisoners confined in the depôt of the prefecture. Some of my Cossacks accompanied them to see whether there might be among them any ex-companions at the hulks or prison, who had concealed themselves under false names, in order to escape the maximum of punishment which justice allots to relapsed convicts. This visit was called by the detectives "doing the depôt," but the robbers in their picturesque and figurative language, used to say that they were going to "pass the censorship."

Rounds were made daily through Paris and the suburbs, where criminals lounge and spend the day in drinking, while waiting till night allows them to slip into town and attempt some criminal trick. The informers marched ahead, and the agents followed about fifty yards behind, nothing showing that they were in any way connected together. When the first met any escaped convict, or any man who had broken his ban, he quickly raised his hat or cap in a certain manner; then the agents walked up and arrested the man, who was completely ignorant by whom he was denounced, or how they had managed to discover him. This was called "doing the St. John."

My Cossacks never assisted the police agents under any circumstances; they never aided in an arrest; they were never asked to join in any important operation, and they were ever passive instruments in the hands of my agents, acting according to the orders given them, just as the ox obeys the goad, but thus composing an exclusive and most secret surveillance, intended to act as an appendix to the police, and not to represent it, as was the case under Vidocq and his successor, Coco Latour.

When a professional robber spends money and leads a jolly life, it is because he has committed a robbery. I had, therefore, the greatest interest in knowing exactly who were flush, and, thanks to my Cossacks, I was constantly posted as to their daily deeds and actions.

Independent of my Cossacks, I had a secret police, composed of liberated convicts, who were under surveillance and were living in the capital without leave, but whose regular conduct proved that repentance had entered their hearts, for each of them worked, either in a shop or at home, according to his trade. Every week, I discreetly inquired of their masters or comrades whether they worked regularly and had regained habits of honesty. After referring to the prefect of police, I allowed some of these persons to remain temporarily in the capital, upon the express condition that they should spend the whole week at work, and employ their Sunday in the service of the police, by taking a walk on that day, either in Paris or the suburbs, and sending me a report in writing on Monday, in which they scrupulously informed me of meetings with old companions, or any schemes of robbery they might have heard of. These men, perfect strangers to the police and the public, rendered me great services, for through their position they attracted the confidence of robbers, who, believing that they had also broken their bans, did not hesitate to avow their designs, and propose to them to take part in their schemes. This secret police secured me many important captures, which cost very little, as I merely granted a premium for each arrest made.

When I took the head of the detective branch, Paris and the suburbs were infested by criminals of every description, who hoped to profit by the disorder which accompanies every revolution. There was not a day or night during which robberies did not take place in Paris, while the roads leading to the capital daily witnessed highway assaults and plunder.

Under these circumstances I sent for all the declarations of robberies committed during the past year. I soon acquired a certainty that there must be several associations of criminals working the capital and the suburbs, but unconnected together. As I had at my disposal but a very limited number of agents, I selected twelve whom I took under my own special direction, and began hunting down the rogues who at night plundered the shops of jewellers, goldsmiths, &c., whose articles had an intrinsic value, and could be easily melted down. On the night of February 9th, 1849, a considerable burglary was committed at a jeweller's in the Palais Royal, and my predecessor had made every effort to discover the burglars, but in vain. I began investigations in my turn, which soon taught me that an ex-convict of the name of G—— resided at Montmartre. I had long been acquainted with his cleverness, and hence the idea occurred to me that he might be a receiver to the daring thieves, and I sent an inspector to watch his house and arrest any suspicious person who went there. At about eight in the evening my agents apprehended a man in a state of intoxication, and in possession of a bundle of false keys. He was immediately brought to my office, and I tried to obtain some information from the man, who was temporarily deprived of reason. It was fortunate that I did so, for I soon learned from him who he was: I held, in fact, the leader of the band, Pierre Leveille, thirty-six years of age, and a very sharp fellow. He had lived in Paris for several years, and had been condemned to eight years' penal servitude for robbery. On the expiration of his sentence he broke his ban, and had set to work again at his old game with very considerable skill. He gave me the names and addresses of his accomplices and receivers, as well as that of the locksmith who made the false keys. The total number amounted to twenty-six persons. Three days after, they were all locked up simultaneously to wait for the assizes.

So soon as this band was disposed of, I set to work actively in discovering another association of a far more dangerous character, whose deeds were daily recorded in the newspapers. In 1848, numerous highway robberies had produced a terror in the parishes adjoining Paris ; daily or rather nightly new attacks took place ; every day fresh victims came to complained and there seemed no prospect of the evil being checked.

Two persons had been described to the police, who; with unparalleled boldness and success, hid on the roads, and arrested vehicles, principally those in which farmers were returning from market with the proceeds of their sales. One of the two villains clambered into the cart from behind, and adroitly threw round the driver's neck a cord which pulled him violently back, while the other villain got up in front and plundered the hapless victim of money and watch ; and at times, owing to the tension from the rope, the sufferer's face turned blue, the blood poured from his nostrils, and he was all but strangled. It was no longer money or life, but money and life.

At other times, when the use of the cord was not possible, owing to the construction of the vehicle, the villains employed a knife or a pistol to intimidate the travellers. Lastly, the crime sometimes assumed melodramatic proportions, for the adventurers carried on their trade with blackened faces. Among their exploits I will quote the following specimen of their mode of operation.

On March 17, 1848, Madame Bertha, wife of a small farmer at Villetaneuve, was proceeding home quietly in a cart with her daughter. All at once, at about nine in the evening, her horse shied and stopped, a man with blackened face pointed a pistol at the woman and shouted, "It is time." At this signal, another man, also with blackened face, who held a monstrous knife between his teeth, leapt upon the front of the cart, and held out his cap. Madame Bertha eagerly threw into it all the small change she had; but this did not suit the robbers, who, though very willing to receive small coins, preferred large. The man with the knife, therefore, said to the woman, "This is not enough, we know that you have more than this," and she at once threw all her money into the cap. The robbers, at length satisfied, went off, courteously wishing their victim a good night and pleasant dreams.

On the 25th, a powerful carter of Meulan, who was returning to his master's house with his cart, noticed two men going the same road, at one moment behind, at another before, him, and apparently talking very earnestly on business matters. At ten o'clock he reached the demi-lane of Naunterre, a place generally deserted at so late an hour. The pedestrians here suddenly came up, and one of them put a pistol to the carter's chest, saying, "You must give us your money, or you are a dead man." The startled man made no attempt at defence, and the second assailant searched him and took from him a purse containing 210 francs.

On the 28th of the same month, the two men attacked a couple of women on the Montmorency road, who were returning home in their cart. At about half-past eight in the evening, a man came up to the cart, who tried to get up a conversation by asking where they were going. Madame Tuleux's reply was to give her horse a smart lash, and it started at a gallop; but one hundred and fifty yards further on, the vehicle was arrested by another individual, who held a pistol at the two females. The first man ran up, mounted the step, and received from the women all they possessed, and then both bandits disappeared.

Owing to these repeated complaints, I sent a party of agents supported by irregular Cossacks to explore that portion of the suburb formed by La Chapelle, Montmartre, and their dependencies, in order to discover whether any suspicious persons lived there. After two days' investigation, the sergeant intrusted with the search came to tell me that two men lived at No. 3, Rue des Clayes, one of whom went by the name of Dupont, the other by that of Charles, called the Flea. They had no trade or work, and yet seemed to live at their ease; they each kept a mistress, spent nearly the whole night away from home, and returned in the morning with a full bag, which they had been seen to take out empty. I established a watch, and at three the next morning my agents arrested the so-called Dupont, at the moment when he returned with the stolen objects, and brought him to the prefecture. When questioned about his means of existence, he asserted that he picked up bullets at the St. Ouen targets; but he was soon recognised as one Michaut, who had already undergone degrading punishments on several occasions. A trap was set at his domicile, and his accomplice, Pellé by name, was apprehended in his turn. I then examined all the déclarations of highway robberies made, compared the imperfect descriptions made by the victims with those of these two men, and felt convinced that they were the criminals. Besides, I questioned the first prisoner in such a way that he was forced to yield to the evidence, and resolved to speak. Michaut, after confessing to me that he and Pellé were the originators of all the highway robberies, denounced to me all his accomplices, as well as the receivers of the stolen property, who were all arrested.

The examination revealed a number of unrecorded robberies, but among them is one which deserves to be quoted for its originality. On the night of February 23, 1848, a sleepless night for many, Michaut, Pellé, and men of the names of Rivals, Picard, and Casse-Tuile, attacked the guard at Monceaux, and disarmed them, and, then, representing the armed force, ordered to watch over the repose and safety of all, they attacked the shop of a curiosity dealer, under the excuse of obtaining arms. The shutters were smashed in by their repeated blows, and Rivals took out a case containing ten watches, which disappeared in his pockets, and were afterwards divided among the thieves. Michaut and Pellé were sentenced to penal servitude for life, Rivals to eight years of the same penalty, and the rest to minor punishments.

Levielle's band was arrested four days after my appointment as chief detective. The incarceration of Michaut and his companions took place toward the end of March; but all was not finished yet. Every night shops were broken into and plundered, and new complaints daily taught me that I must increase my vigilance.

I had to no purpose sent out my best agents. In vain did I send my irregular Cossacks all over Paris and the suburbs, for no result satisfied my expectations, and my men were beginning to feel discouraged. One evening my memory and reflection enabled me to lay hands on the chief of the band whom I had so long sought, and who was a celebrity among his fellows. It was April 16; I had, as usual, left my office at eleven at night to go home to my lodgings at No. 1, Rue Lenoir, and on reaching the corner of my street, a few minutes before midnight, I noticed two men in blouses conversing quietly in front of a broker's shop. The sight of two men standing on the pavement and conversing is not very extraordinary, for I every night saw at the corner of my street half-drunken workmen or rag-pickers talking and quarrelling. I fancied that these two men had just left a a disreputable ball-room in the street; but what struck me was the voice of one of them, which was not strange to me. I tried to recal this voice, and under what circumstances I had heard it, and I soon had it all. It was the voice of a very tall, muscular man, with an olive complexion, who had been indicated to me as an ex-convict under rupture of ban. I had had him arrested and brought to my office a few days before, when he handed me a perfectly regular passport with the name of Samson. The search made for this name in the judicial registers had led to no result, and when confronted with my Cossacks, they did not recognise my man, so that I was compelled to set him at liberty. On reaching my door, I turned round to have a last look, and noticed that Samson's companion was following me. This led me to think that I had been recognised by the latter, and he had me followed to see where I was going; but I presently learned that I was mistaken in this supposition.

At seven o'clock, the next morning, when I left my house to go to the office, I noticed a large crowd opposite the broker's, the front door of whose shop had been broken open. Madame Lebel, on seeing me, came up crying, and said that thieves had broken in during the night and entirely stripped her shop. I left her with a promise to pay especial attention to the affair. From this moment I felt certain that Samson was one of the robbers. On reaching the office, I selected two of my strongest agents, and sent them to Samson's lodgings, with orders to bring him to me at once, if he were at home, or to wait for him if he were not so. My robber, who had been out all night, returned to his lodging at eleven a.m., and, after being arrested, he came to my office with a smiling face, and that assurance which is produced either by a good conscience or a most perfect villany.

"Samson," I said to him without further preface, "you and some other individuals robbed last night the broker at the corner of the Rue Lenoir."

"I, sir?" he answered; "you are mistaken."

"Do not say that; you entered the shop by breaking pen the front door."

"I assure you that you are mistaken; I was not even aware that there was a broker where you mention, or that he had been robbed."

"And I assure you that you are the burglar, because at midnight last night when I turned into the Rue Lenoir to go to my lodgings, you were talking in front of the broker's door with another man, who, by the way, followed me; probably by your orders to see where I was going."

"Well, sir, I repeat that you are mistaken, and that the person whom you fancied you recognised was not I."

"But where did you spend the night?"

"At Paul Niquet's in the Halle."

Seeing that I could get nothing out of him, while convinced that I had to do with a clever professional robber, it occurred to me that the passport under which he sheltered himself might not belong to him, or at any rate had been obtained in a false name. Consequently, I had Samson again looked at by my Cossacks and the informers in the Conciergerie, but with no result: and in my desperation I had the registers again searched for any description which might tally with that of my man. Samson, with his tall stature, olive complexion, and thick black hair, bore an extraordinary likeness to a man of the name of Alexander Puteaux, a liberated convict from Brest, who had broken his ban. I therefore sent for him to my office, and said to him with a smile:

"Tell me, Master Samson, did you ever know any person of the name of Puteaux?"

"Come, come," he answered, "that will do. I see that I am recognised and denial is of no avail. Well, yes, what you said about the robbery of that night is exact, and I committed it; but you are mistaken about yourself, for I did not recognise you. My comrade followed you for the purpose of settling you with an iron crowbar he had under his blouse, if he had seen you going towards the guardhouse to have us arrested, so you had a lucky escape."

Then he added,

"I know that you are a worthy man who always keep the promises you make, and so I will be frank with you and tell you all. At one in the morning, Janin and I broke into the shop, and then our comrades arrived. We made the contents of the shop into bundles, and carried them off in three sacks to our usual receiver."

"Where does he live? who is he?"

"Roussille, the second-hand dealer at No. 4, Rue du Plâtre St. Jacques. The bargain is not concluded, and we have only received 200 francs on account."

He then gave me the names of his five accomplices, who were arrested on the same day, as were Roussille and his wife. The latter, when confronted with Puteaux, refused to recognise him, and made a dreadful row when he spoke to them about the receiving. In vain did he recal the facts connected with the last delivery, in vain did he mention special circumstances which proved their complicity: they persisted in their denial and demanded a search of their shop, which led to no discovery.

While this was going on, Madame Lebel and her two daughters arrived, and implored Madame Roussille to state where the goods were, as the loss of them would ruin them completely. The scene lasted for nearly three hours, with alternations of tears and denials. My heart bled and Puteaux himself was disgusted, when a clerk came to tell me that a person wished to speak with me.

"Tell him that I am busy, and cannot see him at present: he can wait or call again."

The clerk took back my answer, but the stranger insisted on seeing me upon a matter of the deepest importance. I therefore ordered him to be shown in.

"I am a carpenter, sir," he said to me, "and a near neighbour of Roussille, in the Rue du Plâtre. Hearing that he and his wife were arrested, I have come to declare to you that M. Roussille, this very morning, asked me to keep for him, for a little while, a number of sacks filled with goods, and in feeling these sacks I noticed in one of them an iron crowbar. You can suppose that I have not the slightest wish to be compromised in the affair."

This statement put an end to the impudent denials

of the Roussilles. I went to the carpenter's with a police commissioner, and we seized the goods, which were recognised as the property of Madame Lebel. In spite of their apparently small trade, the Roussilles also bought, on terms very advantageous for themselves, plate and jewellery, and after melting them down, sold them to a dealer in bullion. A search in their domicile led to the seizure of two of these ingots, as well as of various articles of jewellery which they had not been able to place in the melting-pot.

The examination, and the search made, enabled us to trace the perpetrators of a great number of robberies committed with aggravating circumstances in Paris and the suburbs. Consequently Puteaux, Janin, and their accomplices, twenty-six in number, including the Roussilles, and two women of bad character, who got rid of stolen property either by selling or pledging it, were brought to trial. Puteaux had twenty years, and the rest varying terms of penal servitude.

I had thus picked up seventy-four prisoners on these expeditions; but for all that, the number of robberies did not decrease; on the contrary, they merely assumed a different shape. This time the doors did not show the slightest sign of breaking in, but the most complicated and secret locks were opened without an effort. On April 14, 1849, one of my Cossacks met two old companions at the hulks, of the names of

Dumont and Moser, who believing him to be like themselves, approached him unsuspectingly, and proposed to have a bottle with him. So soon as they were cozily seated in a wine-shop, tongues became loosened, confidence was restored, and the fellows began describing their projects.

"Will you join us?" Moser suddenly asked my Cossack. "To-morrow morning we are going to plunder the room of a journeyman butcher, in the Rue St. Amboise."

"I would do so with pleasure, old fellow," the denouncer replied; "but I have an engagement for to-morrow with two college companions, to pass an hour at the apartments of a swell, who spends his Sunday regularly with a clergyman in the country."

"No matter, you will find us here to-night if your affair does not come off. You can join us all the same."

At night, when my three convicts were seated at the wine dealer's, I sent one of my agents, by the Cossack's advice, to have a look at Dupont and Moser. The agent went up to the waiter, told him about an imaginary bet, and obtained leave to take his place for a moment. Ere long, my agent, with an apron and cap on and sleeves turned up, was serving a bottle of wine to the three friends, and stamping on his memory the faces of the two rogues.

At four o'clock the next morning, an inspector with

four agents stationed themselves in the neighbourhood of the indicated house. At seven o'clock they saw two persons enter it; they were Moser and Dupont. In a few minutes the agents saw them come out again and supposed that the robbery was effected; so they let them go a few yards, then arrested them, and took them to the nearest guard-house. While the two robbers were being searched, a woman came to inform the agents that a man, apparently an accomplice of the arrested persons, was watching in front of the house in which the robbery had been committed. Two agents at once went off to arrest the third man: on reaching the house, they found a very well-dressed man, who, on feeling himself collared, shouted furiously that there must be some mistake: he gave himself out as a respectable tradesman in the quarter, and called to his help the journeymen butchers present, who, taking his part, enabled him to escape from the agents' hands. Profiting by this moment of liberty, our self-called tradesman drew a dagger and a pistol from under his clothes, and then fled at full speed in the same direction by which the agents had come, and thus ran right into the arms of their two colleagues, who were hastening to their assistance on hearing their shouts. After an obstinate struggle they at length succeeded in mastering him. The butchers, who had helped his flight believing him an honest man, rushed upon him when they learned he was a thief, and one of them, who had a chopper in his hand, would have cut him over the head with it had not one of the agents caught his arm. When led to the post and searched, there were found upon him, in addition to the dagger and pistol, some false keys newly made, a gold watch and chain, two purses, one containing 160 francs in gold, while another amount of 200 francs was found in his boots. Morer had in his pocket a crowbar, and Dupont eight false keys and a cold chisel.

When these arrests had been made, the agents went to the house which the agents had entered, but not a sign of a burglary could be found. Moser and Dupont, when questioned on the point, declared that they had certainly entered the house for the purpose of commiting a robbery, but struck by the poor appearance of the interior, they resolved not to make any attempt, but went away, as they came, empty-handed. On being brought to my office, they repeated their statement, and declared that they did not know the third person arrested, and had never seen him before. When they were taken to the lock-up, I had the third man brought in, who presented himself with great assurance, stated that his name was Daufier, and protested against the violence of which he considered himself the victim. But this tissue of falsehoods was soon destroyed by the truth, for the perfectly honest man was recognised as one Renaud, an ex-convict of Brest, standing under police surveillance, and guilty of breaking his ban to come to the capital.

Although he had served no apprenticeship to the trade, Renaud manufactured his own false keys, and most certainly those found in his possession were little masterpieces. Among others, one was most remarkable for its finish and delicacy of manufacture: he had christened this Joséphine, and said that he would back himself to open eight locks out of ten with it. It could be enlarged or reduced as was required, and could be made to fit almost any keyhole. Provided with such cleverly made instruments, Renaud was the more dangerous, because he also possessed an easy manner, an excellent delivery, and a demeanour which seemed to denote the man of fashion. Thanks to his advantageous exterior, which was heightened by a very careful attire, our robber boldly presented himself at the best houses, and passed the porter's lodge without exciting the slightest suspicion. Renaud, after committing a considerable robbery, went to spend the summer in the country a few miles from Paris; he visited the best society, and passed himself off as a rich Parisian, who preferred green fields to the dust of the Boulevards. He was on the point of marrying a wealthy young lady, when he suddenly disappeared—his purse was drained, and he was compelled to line it again. His mode of working was by going up a staircase and rapping at a door: if he was answered, he asked for Mr. So-and-so, who generally lived on the floor above or below, whose name he had been careful to obtain from the directory. If there was no answer, he at once produced his keys: he opened the door and closed it again immediately. Once master of the situation, Renaud searched everywhere, took whatever he thought proper, and then went away, closing the door after him.

On learning that Renaud had lived with his cousin-german in the Rue St. Jacques, I thought myself bound, out of prudence, to arrest the latter as well as his wife, for they might be possibly accomplices or receivers. While this arrest was being effected, Renaud, seated in my office, was talking with me as if he were a simple visitor, and the subject of conversation had not been his own arrest. He was ignorant, however, that Moser and Dupont had not committed the projected robbery. "I know my fate," he said to me. "I shall be sentenced to twenty years' penal servitude as a relapsed convict; but I don't care for that, a little more or a little less, for I shall never leave the hulks."

"Why not?"

"Oh, I have my own condemnation inside me; I have but a few years to live. I am suffering from consumption, and shall not get over it."

"Well, it will certainly be more agreeable for you

to do your sentence in a Paris prison, where you will be far more comfortable than at the hulks. Confess, and I will promise to manage the affair."

"Confess! Well, that is not so very difficult; but whether I am concerned in one robbery or fifty, the punishment will be the same, as I am a relapsed convict."

At this moment my office door opened, and his cousin, Madame M——, was brought in. She was short, but her whole person was marked with extraordinary distinction, and her large eyes, which were remarkably fine, seemed trying to read the thoughts of those whom she looked at.

"Come," said Renaud to me, "if you will promise me to set my cousin at liberty, I will confess anything you please. I pledge you my word of honour that she is perfectly innocent in all this."

Renaud's word of honour! Still I made no objection to the pledge, and after assuring him that his cousin should be released, he at once revealed a dozen robberies, committed with false keys, in which, however, he denied that he had had any accomplice. He coolly declared himself to be a professional robber; and he prided himself on the boldness and skill he had displayed in effecting his criminal designs alone.

The next day I sent for Renaud, that he might continue his revelations, and, after answering several of my questions, he remarked with admirably feigned simplicity, "Monsieur Canler, you had better seize a great number of objects stolen by me, which are deposited in a room I hired for the purpose in the Faubourg Montmartre. I forget the name of the street, but, if you will have me taken there, I will point it out to your agents." I had him placed in a fiacre with three agents, whom I ordered not to leave him, even for the most pressing wants. Renaud was scarcely in the vehicle ere he complained of a violent colic; his sufferings appeared intolerable, and on reaching the Rue Lamartine, and the room which he pointed out, his first request was to be allowed to retire. The agents, remembering my orders, would not leave him, although Renaud tried a thousand schemes to get rid of them, saying, for instance, "You can surely remain at the door, for I shall not fly away." One of the agents went in with him, and it was fortunate he did so, for the iron bars closing the window had been removed: this window looked upon a little roof, from which it would be easy to leap down into the courtyard and escape. On inquiry it was learned that the room had been occupied by a convict of the name of Faligaud, a friend of Renaud, who had only moved on the previous day, and had probably prepared this way of escape for his comrade.

When the agents told me of this affair on their return, I said to Renaud, "So you wanted to play us a trick?"

"What would you have?" he replied, laughingly; "the police and the thieves are continually playing at prisoner's base, and the cleverest man catches the other. This time you were cleverer than I, that is all."

A fortnight after this arrest, on May 4th, 1849, Paris celebrated the festival of the Constitution. The day terminated with a magnificent display of fire-works, and an immense crowd collected in the Champs Elysées to admire the fairy like illuminations. Amongst the promenaders were three men, not there for their amusement, but whose character it would have been impossible to detect: they were a sergeant of detectives and two inspectors, my agents, whose duty it was to watch the crowd, and stop the pranks of the pick-pockets, and they were talking about one thing and the other while looking around them scrutinizingly. For a long time an individual of the name of Godmus had been described to the police as one of the most dangerous robbers in the capital; liberated from Brest in the previous January, he had broken his ban to come to Paris, where, owing to his remarkable skill, he had hitherto contrived to elude the active search made after him. All at once one inspector said to the other:—

"I have just seen Godmus on the other side of the way."

"It is certainly he," said his companion. "Let us cross and take him."

But they were obliged to employ great precautions in approaching him, for they knew him to be armed and a very dangerous fellow. Godmus was a man endowed with athletic strength : large moustaches, an upright walk, and a coat buttoned to the chin, gave him a thoroughly military aspect, while, to add to the illusion, he impudently wore in his button-hole a wide red ribbon, the insignia of the Legion of Honour. The agents rushed upon him and threw their arms around him, but, rapid though the movement was, Godmus was able to draw a pistol from his pocket and cock it, though it was luckily taken from him before he could do any mischief. The struggle went on most obstinately, and the sergeant having accidentally raised his hand to a level with the convict's mouth, the latter seized one of his fingers and bit it to the bone; then, seeing the promenaders collect round him, he had recourse to a very common trick of the time : "Citizens," he exclaimed, "citizens, help ! I was condemned by default in the June insurrection, and do not allow a political accused to be ill-treated !" But this appeal met with no echo in the crowd, and the agents succeeded in conveying Godmus to the prefecture, where he was searched. There were found on him a dagger and a clasp-knife, as well as papers belonging to one Porchereau, which were the produce of a robbery. Temporarily confined at La Force, this audacious criminal found himself there at the same time as

Renaud, with whom I had locked up a spy, with orders to discover his accomplices, were it possible. One day, while they were walking in the airing-yards, only separated by a partition wall, the spy picked up on the ground a "postilion," which Godmus had just thrown over the wall. A postilion is simply a ball of bread-crumb, containing a note addressed to a prisoner with whom it is impossible to communicate otherwise, and which is sent to him, either through an open window or in any other way, in order to warn him of what he is to say when examined, or of something else to his advantage. The copy of this note was immediately sent to me, and it revealed the existence of a lodging common to both prisoners, which undeniably proved a complicity which we had hitherto been unable to establish. Henceforth the trial assumed a new phase, and Godmus was inculpated in Renaud's offences. A search at their common domicile soon led to the arrests of the M——s, husband and wife, as well as of a fifth accomplice, a man of the name of Faligand, to whom I have already referred on the subject of the attempted escape from the Rue Lamartine.

Since his arrest, Renaud had also attempted to assassinate a gendarme who was taking him before the magistrate, and at the same time we obtained certain information that Godmus had been guilty of a similar attempt on the person of one Rouchon. They were all tried at the next assizes; the two first prisoners were sentenced to penal servitude for life, Faligand, as a relapsed convict, to twenty years, while the M—— —s were acquitted.

The chase of those robbers who were not afraid of the assize court was not the only one to which I had to devote myself, for it was urgent to get hold of the fellows who merely commit offences which come under the cognizance of the magistrate.

The ring-droppers, &c., who, worn out by the pursuit to which they had been previously exposed, left the capital in disgust, eagerly returned after the events of February. The police had been warned of their presence by a large number of robberies, in which were employed the well-known tricks, which, in spite of the publicity so frequently given them for the benefit of the public, still find dupes. This may be explained, however, by the skill with which these rogues manage to excite the cupidity of the persons whom they intend to plunder. The arrest of scamps of this class had become much more difficult since prudence had caused them to take various precautions to escape from the police. Hence they were careful never to live in the heart of Paris, and only to enter town disguised; and when they had found their victim they led him to some remote spot, and generally hired a fiacre, in order to be safe from my agents. Once the robbery was performed, they hurriedly left Paris, and continued their malpractices in the provinces.

At nine o'clock on the evening of March 15th, 1849, I was proceeding to the Elysée by order, and on passing through the Rue de Faubourg St. Honoré, I noticed three persons whose faces I could not distinguish in the darkness, but the voice of one of them appeared familiar to me. He was a fellow of the name of Seutin, who had been convicted several times for sharping, and who joined to extraordinary skill all the roguery of lengthened experience. I at once suspected that he had caught a pigeon to pluck, and hence, leaving him to carry out his scheme before I arrested him, I passed the party, and hid myself in a gateway so as to see everything without being seen. I easily succeeded in concealing myself from them. Thus, I saw them converse for a while, and afterwards turn into the Rue de la Madeleine, where I followed them in the shadow of the houses; when they reached the other end of the street they separated. I suspected that the trick had been done, and so I ran after my sharper, who was walking along very quietly, and collared him while saying—

"In the name of the law, I arrest you."

Seutin, continuing to play the American, said, "Aho! you say——"

"You will follow me to the guard-house, and a little quicker, then."

"Môsieu! I told you that——" And my false American began raising cries of alarm, while impudently asserting that he was an honest, peaceful citizen of the United States, recently arrived at Paris, and who had no concern with the police. On hearing these cries and imprecations, which he addressed to the passers-by with an effrontery which he derived from the thought that he was not recognised, a good many persons began to collect, and I could already hear the crowd murmuring at this pretended violation of the law of nations, and the clumsiness of the agent who was guilty of it. Now it is only a step from blaming to assisting, and fearing lest some hotheaded fellows might enable my prisoner to escape, I raised my voice, and said to him—"Ah! Master Seutin, you wish to pass for an honest, peaceful citizen? It is very smart, but it is unlucky for you that the head of the detective staff should have passed, and recognised you as a thief! Now, gentlemen," I said to the persons who surrounded us, "are there any of you willing to assist me in taking this thief to the guard-house?"

Enlightened by this appeal, Seutin's victim himself eagerly lent me a hand, and the sharper was soon put in a place of surety. When brought before the sessions he was sentenced to ten years' imprisonment. Such was the arrest of the first sharper, and within six weeks ten other thieves à l'Americaine, and ninety-two liberated convicts who had broken their ban, were convicted.

CHAPTER XX.

THE POIRIER-DESFONTAINES MURDER.

At No. 422, Rue de St. Honoré, there was a fashionable shop for bronzes, the owner of which, M. Poirier-Desfontaines, an old bachelor, had only one servant, a young man of twenty, short, beardless, and weak-looking, who enlisted in the Garde Mobile in 1848, and was only too glad to throw away his uniform at the expiration of his engagement. At the close of December, 1850, he entered M. Poirier's service, and on the following January 6, he was seen to open and clean the shop as usual; then he went out, but soon returned with a trunk, which he carried up to his master's rooms on the first floor. Only a few hours had elapsed when he told the porter's daughter that his master had gone to spend four or five days in the country, and that he was going to carry him some clothes which he wanted. At 2, p.m., he closed the shop, called a porter to help him down with the large trunk which he had brought in the morning, and then, engaging two other strange porters who were passing with a truck, the trunk was placed upon the latter, and he left the house, telling all whom it might concern that he was going to join his master.

On the day after this departure the neighbours and the porter felt uneasy at this sudden disappearance of both master and man. The dealer in bronzes had not accustomed them to such freaks, and they considered it extraordinary that such a quiet, regular, and domesticated man as M. Poirier should have left his house so suddenly. The porter informed the police commissioner, who came to the house, but went away again, as the porter had peeped through a hole, and noticed that everything was in its place.

Several days elapsed, during which the public curiosity and impatience gradually increased, and the suspicions of the neighbours were directed to a murder. The authorities turned their attention to the affair, and the police commissioner returned, and this time resolved to break open the door. Then spots of blood on the boards, as well as a blood-stained hammer, proved that murder had been committed, but the body got rid of. Active and incessant researches were made, without success, however, until on January 30, the manager of the Châteauroux railway informed the police prefect that on the 6th of the month a trunk had been sent from Paris, addressed to a M. Moreau, 22, Grande Rue, Châteauroux ; but as the consignee could not be found, the trunk had been brought back to Paris, and a notice forwarded to the sender, who was equally unknown at the address which he had given. This coincidence aroused suspicion. The magistrate proceeded to the station, had the trunk opened, and saw in it to his horror the corpse of a dressed man, whose legs were doubled up by a rope passed round the neck and fastened to the right thigh. The head and trunk were at the bottom, and the skull was fractured in several places. By the side of the corpse, which was already in a state of putrefaction, were an unmarked shirt and a pair of trousers stained with blood, which had probably belonged to the assassin, who had doubtless considered this the most simple way to get rid of them.

When confronted with the corpse, the porter of the house recognised the clothes that covered the body as belonging to his tenant, M. Poirier. From this moment the police turned their exclusive attention to the missing servant. The porters who had carried the trunk were discovered with great difficulty, and they stated that the trunk had been left at a coach office in the Rue Croix des Petits Champs, where it was also learned the man who sent the trunk to Châteauroux took a seat for himself in the Marseilles diligence, under the name of Viou. It was also learned that he returned to the office an hour later, and inquired whether the Marseilles coach passed through Tours, and on receiving a reply in the negative, he had his luggage conveyed by a porter to the Orleans railway station. This porter was discovered, and when questioned as to the person whose luggage he had carried, he replied that he was a short young man, who accompanied him as far as the St. Mandé bridge, and then left him to do the rest of the distance alone. This information left me no doubt as to the culpability of Viou, and taking advantage of his liberty to go in and out at all hours, he had surprised and murdered his master.

But where was the assassin? had he, as circumstances seemed to prove, immediately left the capital, to seek in the provinces or a foreign land a refuge which Paris could not offer him? Ought I to seek him at Tours, for which city he seemed to have a peculiar predilection? or was I to regard his marches and counter-marches as a feint intended to throw the police out, and insure himself an undisturbed security in Paris? All these hypotheses presenting themselves in turn to my mind, I invented a stratagem which would serve the double purpose of bringing him back to Paris, if he were in the country, and making him remain in the capital, if he had not quitted it. I knew by experience that all criminals daily read attentively several newspapers, at the head of which I placed the *Gazette des Tribunaux*, for they are anxious to know as exactly as possible what is being said and known about their crime and themselves, and then act according to circumstances. I was fully persuaded that Viou would not depart from this system, and hence begged M. Horace Raisson, editor of the Gazette, to be kind enough to insert at the end of the report about the discovery of M. Poirier's body, and its identification, the words, *the murderer at once proceeded to Spain.* In accordance with my instructions, the Editor ended his article as follows :—

"As for the perpetrator of the crime, the telegraph has been set to work to forward his description to the frontiers, in the improbable event that he has not yet gone to a foreign country. Different signs, and especially the two trunks which he carried away on his flight, will aid in all probability, in coming upon his track, if he has proceeded to Spain, as his first movements would seem to indicate."

On the same day I had occasion to see M. Carlier, the prefect of police.

"Ah, Canler," he said, on perceiving me ; "do you think that newspapers are of any use ?"

"At times, sir."

"Well, then, read this one, and it will tell you where the murderer of M. Poirier is at this moment ; these fellows appear to be better informed than we are."

While saying this he handed me the number of the Gazette in which was the sentence which I have just quoted, and said, anxiously,

"I am afraid this villain will escape us."

"On the contrary, M. le Préfet, for I reckon on that article to deliver him to me."

"What do you mean?"

"Something very simple; the article you have just read is of my invention. Up to the present I have been fishing in troubled water, I do not know whether Viou has remained in Paris or gone into the country, consequently, as my investigations have no certainty, and are only based on probabilities, they can produce no satisfactory result; but after this article, which Viou will read, and which he most assuredly has read by this time, he will fancy that, as he is being sought for in all directions, there is no place of safety for him but Paris, and he will of his own accord, I hope, thrust his head down the wolf's throat."

In fact, Viou, on reading the article in the Gazette, hurriedly returned to Paris, where he fancied himself in greater safety. A few days later I learned that he was living at No. 21, Rue du Pont Louis Philippe, and I at once went there with two agents, but the murderer was out. After passing the night at a public ball, he returned home at about five in the morning, with one of those nymphs who, having no titular lover, convert the wild youths of our capital into one immense seraglio, where they select according to their momentary caprice. At about nine o'clock Viou went out with this woman, informing the porter that he should not be back till night. I went to his room, and on entering it, I recognised at the first glance, the cane and bag of M. Poirier, objects described as having been stolen by the assassin; and over the mantelpiece I found two pistols loaded to the muzzle. I then explained to the porter that his tenant was the murderer of the dealer in bronzes, of the Rue St. Honoré, and told him that, in order to avoid any species of indiscretion which might compromise the success of the affair, he must not think it extraordinary if my agents did not leave him for a moment.

At eleven at night, Viou came in, and asked the porter for his key; but the latter, on seeing him, called out, as was agreed with my agents, "M. Viou!" The two agents leaped on the assassin, tied his hands before he had time to look round, and conveyed him to the Conciergerie, whither I proceeded at once. Viou was searched, and there was found on him a sum of six hundred and fifty francs, in gold, a hair-ring, and a gold watch, which had belonged to his victim. I sent my prisoner to the depôt, and gave orders that he should be watched most strictly, to prevent any attempt at suicide.

Night brings counsel, it is said, and hence, when Viou was brought to my office the next morning, that I might cross-question him, I saw a young man, with a calm air and tranquil face, who positively denied that he was the murderer of M. Poirier, and accounted for that event, and his possession of things which had belonged to his master, in the following way :—

"On January 6th, I had just opened the shop, when two men came up to me and asked to see my master. I showed them up to the first floor, as he was still in his bed-room, and went down to the shop again. But soon after I heard a great noise over my head ; I went up to see what was going on, and perceived my poor master lying lifeless on the ground ; I was going to shout for help, but the two men seized me, and threatened to kill me also, unless I swore absolute silence. In order to induce me to keep the secret, they gave me one thousand five hundred francs in gold, and several articles which had belonged to my unhappy master. When they had left, as I feared lest I should be made responsible for the crime, I hastily disposed of the body and made my escape."

I tried to make Viou comprehend the absurdity of such a story, and the impossibility of believing such nonsense ; but he persisted in his statement, and assured me that he had only spoken the truth. I had him taken back to the depôt.

In the same manner as certain persons derive distinction from the deeds of their ancestors, and quote the achievements of their fathers as the antecedents of their own exploits, the murderer of M. Poirier-Desfontaines could invoke as a precedent for his conduct the melancholy renown which his father had acquired in the annals of crime. At the period when the son was immured in La Force for murder, the father was undergoing at the central prison of Melun an imprisonment of five years for robbery. In 1830, he had been sentenced to five years' penal servitude; and no sooner was he liberated than he recommenced his culpable practices; and in 1837 was sentenced to another five years' imprisonment for robbery. We see that the son outstripped the father on the road which the latter had traced for him.

The absurd defence Viou invented was destroyed by the evidence collected; and consequently, on April 30th, 1851, the jury found him guilty, and sentence of death was passed upon him. Viou listened to this sentence with an apathy which could only have been expected from a thoroughly brutalized man. Not a muscle of his face quivered. Nothing about him indicated that the sentence just pronounced was the span of his life. At a later date, when informed that his appeal was rejected, he retained the same stoicism and indifference: it seemed as if his crime and his condemnation did not concern him in the slightest degree.

At four o'clock on the morning of June 18th, the turnkey of La Roquette prison went to Viou's cell, and informed him that he had but a few hours still to live. Viou, who was fast asleep when the turnkey entered, rose at once, saying—

"I am ready! I have deserved death, and I feel a horror of my crime!" Then, feeling hungry, as is so often the case with criminals who are resigned to their fate, he asked for food, and ate nearly the whole of a chicken which was brought him. Then, taking off his blouse, he surrendered himself to the executioner's assistants, and said, when they proceeded to tie his hands behind his back, "What is the use of that? Do you think I shall resist you? You are taking a deal of unnecessary trouble."

At four minutes to eight, the procession reached the Barrière St. Jacques, and Viou actively descended from the fatal vehicle.

"Shall I help you to mount?" the executioner asked him.

"Thanks," the condemned man replied; "I can go up perfectly well alone: but be kind enough to remove my cap."

Then he embraced his confessor, hurried up the steps, and before his head was laid on the block he exclaimed, in a loud voice—

"I am willing to die, for I deserve my fate, and I recommend my soul to GOD."

A second later he had ceased to live, and human justice was satisfied. Viou was the last criminal executed at the Barrière St. Jacques; and from the humane point of view, the choice of La Roquette, as the place for executing, is highly laudable. Owing to the proximity of the prison, the last moments of the condemned are soothed as far as possible, his mental torture is diminished, and his agony is restricted to the indispensable preparations.

CHAPTER XXI.

MONOMANIACS.

A STRANGE thing is the human brain! so admirably organized, capable of so much learning, instruction, and reasoning—the creator of sublime resolutions and gigantic labours—adorned with memory, intelligence, and will; but for all that, subjected to such aberrations and hallucinations which often result in madness. Still, before reaching that last stage of wretchedness in which a man loses his senses entirely, and commits a thousand eccentricities, he may be attacked by an affection which has received the name of "monomania" and which is, properly speaking, madness applied to a single thought, a single desire, or a single want.

In some, this monomania is almost invisible, and is a fixed idea turned to one or the other thing: in one it is a fear of robbers; in another, fire; and a third, death; and these three individuals, affected by a different thing, which they conceive to be possible, close at hand and inevitable, mutually ridicule each other, and treat one another reciprocally as monomaniacs. As the preoccupation of such men is constant, more than once individuals afflicted with this infirmity came to my office to claim the help of the police against their vision, or rather against the thing to which they attributed their torture. A few examples will prove the tenacity of the ruling idea, and the regular return of the attacks of such a malady.

A M. V——, a retired cloth-merchant, had been living for several years at the village of Plaisance, with his wife and two daughters, of whom the elder was twenty, the younger eighteen. They were both marriageable; but their worthy father imagined that two individuals, two scamps, armed, as he said, with a "retrospective" mirror of Satanic virtue, came every morning and night to post themselves behind the wall of his house at the hour when his daughters went to bed and rose, and by the help of their mirror were able to see the two girls in an unadorned state.

"You can understand, my dear sir," he added, "how injurious this affair must be to my two daughters, for some one may ask their hand in marriage any day. Well, if this thing were made public, if people were ever to know that they are exposed to the libertine glances of these two vagabonds every morning and night, their reputation would be ruined, and no one would marry them."

I at first soothed his chimera and promised to have the two scamps, whose description he gave, arrested. I believed that I had thus restored calmness to his mind; but a fortnight later I saw my man return, and

I was forced again to hear his lamentations and imprecations against this accursed retrospective mirror, as he called it. This lasted for two years; that is to say, I was annoyed by a visit from him twice a month most regularly. At length, happening to be one day at Plaisance, I resolved to call on the unfortunate man.

"Sir," I said to him, without any preface, "I am the chief detective, and have myself just arrested the two malefactors who dare to insult your daughters, and the retrospective mirror was broken on the spot. As for the scamps, they will have to answer for their conduct before a magistrate."

I do not know whether the sudden announcement of this news produced a salutary effect on M. V——, but from this moment he ceased calling upon me.

I also received visits from a gentleman residing on the Faubourg St. Germain, whose monomania was no less curious. This unfortunate man was persuaded that all the men who met his wife on the staircase of his house behaved to her in the most improper manner, and that boys, paid by his enemies, assailed her so soon as she got into the street, and addressed the coarsest epithets to her. On the first of each month I saw him enter my office; he came with a calm and serious air to beg me to put a stop to this scandal. Each time I assured him that a most rigorous watch should be set, in order to arrest the first individual who had the impudence to commit such an act, and I sent him away quite satisfied. After he had gone, I said to myself, "There, I shall be left alone for a month."

A journeyman locksmith, living at Belleville, came to see me every Sunday morning and beg me to restore his repose, and each time addressed me in the following terms:

"Invisible bells have been hung up in my bed-room by my numerous enemies, who had placed under ground a series of tubes communicating with the Faubourg St. Antoine, and containing electric wires fastened to the bells. I have hardly got into bed ere they all begin a terrific peal. If by chance they stop for a moment, and I fall asleep, they soon begin again, so as to leave me no peace till I have risen."

This maniac's weekly visits lasted for two years, and then suddenly ceased. I learned at a later date that his madness attained such a pitch that it was found necessary to shut him up in Bicetre, where he died shortly after.

But among all the sad stories which display the fragility of man's intellectual organization, the most astounding I ever knew is undoubtedly the following:

One morning my clerk informed me that a gentleman wished to speak with me on a matter of the deepest importance, and I gave orders for him to be shown in. He was a short, stout man in the prime of life, with an open face and penetrating glance.

"I am the most unfortunate of men, sir," he said to

me, confidentially, and in a low voice, as if afraid of being overheard. "I have an excellent business, and a young and pretty wife whom I adore, but she deceives me. I have had the idea of killing her lover, but before proceeding to such an extremity, which would be disastrous to my wife and myself and a scandal for our family, I resolved to come and see you in order to ask you to have my faithless spouse followed and watched, so that she may be surprised with her accomplice."

"Do you know his name?"

"Not at all, sir, for my wife is too crafty to let me discover it. Moreover, I must tell you the entire truth: my wife has a monomania for mankind."

"I do not quite understand you, so be good enough to explain the meaning of those words."

"Well, sir, I repeat it; my wife has a monomania for mankind—that is to say, when she sees a handsome man to her liking, she only thinks, dreams, and aspires to form his acquaintance: then she sets everything at work to produce a *liaison*, and knows no rest till her caprice is satisfied."

"Really, sir, what you are stating is so serious——"

"Yes, yes, and I am most unhappy. As long as it was possible to doubt her infamy, I did so. At a later date I tried to close my eyes and cure her by treating her with the greatest attention, but nothing has succeeded, and so I have come to ask you to have her watched by your agents and detected in the act, for at present I suffer so greatly that I cannot wait any longer."

"Unfortunately, sir, I cannot do what you ask, and you must first make a charge. A magistrate will order an investigation, and issue warrants to arrest the guilty couple, and then, be assured, that I will neglect nothing to satisfy you."

He went away, saying that he would take my advice, and a week later returned, his face beaming with satisfaction, to tell me that he had made a complaint, and the warrants had been issued.

"Well, where are they?" I asked.

"At the Palace of Justice. Be kind enough to send some one to fetch them, for all is in readiness."

I went to inquire at the office, but no complaint had been made, and even my friend's name was unknown. Astonished at the answer given me, I thought that the complainant had committed some error. The next day he entered my office in a state of great excitement, and looking very wretched.

"Can you credit, sir," he said to me, "that this very night my wife's lover entered my house and even that infamous creature's bed-room? This morning, attracted by the noise they were making, I went to the door, which was ajar, and—oh, heavens! just as I was about to enter to chastise the guilty couple and reproach my wife for her abandoned conduct, they made their escape. They have eloped, sir. Yes, she has followed her scoundrelly lover, carrying off every valuable article that she could lay hands on!"

In the presence of such a *dénouement* I could only sympathize with the painful situation of the unfortunate husband; and, after informing him of the answer given me at the office, I urged him to send in a fresh charge. He eagerly accepted my advice, assured me that he would go and give in his charges more fully, and left me, saying that he reckoned on my hearty assistance in getting justice dealt him.

The next day, foreseeing that I should speedily receive orders to pursue the fugitives, I resolved to learn beforehand whether the husband had obtained any further information which might put me on their track: I, therefore, went to his house: he was not in his shop, but a pretty young woman was at the desk.

"M. N—— ?"

"He is out for the moment; but if you have any message for him, I am his wife—"

"You are—his wife?"

"Certainly, sir. What is there so extraordinary in that?"

My amazement—my stupefaction—may be easily conceived.

"Pardon me," I said, regaining my self-possession as well as I could, "but I thought that you had gone —to the country."

"May I ask, sir, who you are?"

"Well, madam, I am the Chief Detective."

"Oh! In that case," she added, with a most gracious smile, "I can understand the whole affair; my husband has probably told you his nonsense. It does not surprise me, for he has threatened to do so for a long time. In the first years of our marriage we were happy, but ere long his jealousy attained such a pitch that his reason became disturbed. At the present day, he sees a lover of mine not only in every man who comes here on business, but also in every passer-by who turns his head to look at the shop."

The information I obtained elsewhere fully confirmed the remarks of this lady, who was justly esteemed by all who knew her. It was only then that I discovered the husband's mental condition, for nothing in his manner, look, or language, revealed the man afflicted with an aberration. Hence I had placed entire confidence hitherto in his statements. A few days after, the poor fellow came to see me again, and I examined him very attentively. His appearance was still the same; but this time he wandered, for he said to me with the utmost coolness—

"Last night, sir, I closed my doors and shutters myself, but unluckily there was a crevice between two planks which I did not notice. My wife's lover took advantage of this crack to enter the house, and even get into her bed."

"I know it," I replied, "but I have just put a stop to it;" and, assuming a confidential tone, I added, "I have just sent two *invisible* agents, who will at once arrest any man who attempts to reach your wife. So, my dear sir, you can now be without fear, and sleep comfortably."

My monomaniac went away enchanted, and exclaiming, "Ah! that is a good idea; I am going to be avenged!"

I did not see him again, and do not know what became of him.

CHAPTER XXII.

A FEMALE DETECTIVE.

At the end of the High-street of la Chapelle, Saint Denis, stood a semi-detached house, only inhabited by Widow Cordier, who was seventy-two years of age, and her grand-nephew, Charles Dutertre, who was not quite ten. The widow had no servant, and was supposed by her neighbours to possess a decent fortune. She was the owner of several houses, and some plots of ground, which produced an excellent rental. In November, 1850, she had received a considerable sum of money, the produce of the sale of one of her pieces of ground; and this money, though known but to few persons, nevertheless became the subject of conversation in the quarter, more than one of the widow's neighbours saying, as they pointed to her windows, "There is a nest of five-franc pieces."

On December 1st our septuagenarian, as well as her nephew, had just retired to bed, when they heard the sound of a window being broken in the room next to theirs. The aunt supposed that the noise was produced by some cat, and got up to drive the intruder away;

but she had scarce opened her bed-room door ere she found herself in the presence of three men, who had broken the pane, pushed back the bolt, and leaped through the window, in order to enter the house. One of them rushed at Madame Cordier, seized her savagely by the throat, laid a hand on her mouth to prevent her from crying out, and throwing her on her back, set his knees on her chest, in order to hold her down. Another held her legs, to keep her from making any movement, and showing her a dagger, said, "You will feel this if you make any row!"

The first assailant ordered her to give up the money which she possessed. On her replying that she only had seven hundred francs, contained in a bag that lay on a table in a room on the first floor, the third malefactor lit a candle which he had brought with him. She then distinctly saw three men, dressed in blouses, and with their faces blackened, to prevent recognition.

The man with the candle entered the widow's bed-room, ordered young Dutertre to take the keys out of his aunt's pocket, to lead him to the first floor, and show him the room in which the money was. Charles obeyed; the robber followed him, and a moment after came down to tell his companions, who still held their victim on the ground, that he had not found the seven hundred francs, and had searched the room in vain. The poor woman was assailed, hereupon, with fresh demands, threats, and violence, which she endured with a courage hardly to be expected from a person of her age.

"Tell us where your money is!"

And the unhappy creature persisted that she had no more than the seven hundred francs she had told them of.

"No arguing," the man who held her feet exclaimed. "Since she will not speak, let us settle her at once."

And the hand round her neck was contracted afresh: a knife flashed in her eyes and descended on her chest; a second later and the crime would probably have been consummated — but in the widow self-preservation had gained the victory, and love of life was more powerful than love of money. She feebly asked leave to speak; and as soon as that was possible, she hastily stated that she had six thousand francs in canvas bags upstairs. The man with the candle went up again with young Dutertre; but either through his eagerness, or some other cause, did not find the money. Hence he came down again, and said to his comrades, "The old she-devil is playing the fool with us, and she must go herself to find the brads." Then the villains allowed the widow to rise; but the struggle she had gone through had so weakened her, that she fell into a chair behind her. They seized her again; and while one of the robbers held her throat to keep her from screaming, another pushed her upstairs. When they reached the room, the old lady removed a pile of haricot beans and displayed seven bags, containing six thousand francs. The robbers took them, carried their victim back to her bedroom, broke open a chest of drawers, in which they hoped to find plate, but only found candles; made the aunt and the nephew go to bed again, and fled with the six thousand seven hundred francs. But little Charles, who had not taken off his trousers when he got into bed, jumped up and ran to shut the yard gates. He there saw the three robbers escaping over the garden-wall.

This scene had lasted no less than three-quarters of an hour: a few minutes later, the widow, who was fearfully bruised by the attempts at strangulation, and who was bleeding at the mouth, collected the little strength left her, and went to ask help of her next-door neighbour. Such were the events, a recital of which soon filled the population of La Chapelle with horror.

Informed of these circumstances, I at once went to the spot to examine the scene of the crime. I saw that the perpetrators must have crossed a hedge, traversed a garden, and scaled another wall, before reaching the house. The manner in which the crime was committed—the circumstances that preceded or accompanied it—the questions and the threats which marked the different phases,—all proved to me that the crime had not been committed by professional burglars, but was rather the handiwork of some lurkers about the Barrière, who had heard by public report of the sum of money which Widow Cordier had received.

I had all the ill-famed houses round Paris explored, first by my ostensible agents, and then by my Cossack irregulars and my Sunday allies. All these researches had led to no result, when, one morning, I heard a sharp discussion in my ante-room. One of the two voices, serious and loud, was that of my clerk; the other, stammering and ropy, was quite strange to me; so I rang the bell.

"What is the matter?"

"There is a drunken woman, whom I cannot manage to turn out, for she insists on speaking to you."

"Let her come in, then."

"But, sir, she——"

"Let her come in! She may have something interesting to communicate to me."

My clerk obeyed with some little repugnance, and I soon saw a woman of about forty stagger in, who, as soon as she had entered my office, made a face at her introducer, saying—

"I told you, my good fellow, that I wished to speak to this gentleman, and that I would speak to him—for I want to be a spy, too."

I invited her to sit down, for she could scarce stand. She was dressed in a poor calico gown, and had a ragged kerchief round her head; but all was stained with wine and mud, and smelt of spirits twenty paces off. The woman's whole appearance was unclean.

"You must not pay attention to my dress," she said, "because I work at the powder-magazine behind the railway."

"What do you want with me?"

"This: I should like to be a police-agent, in order to arrest all the rogues, vagabonds, and thieves in La Villette and La Chapelle,—a heap of good-for-nothing fellows who never work, but always have their pockets full of money."

"Do you know many of them?"

"Many of them! Why, I know them all;—that is why I should like to be a spy, my little darling."

I overlooked the familiarity; and thinking that she might be useful to me in the affair that I was following, I continued—

"Have you heard tell of the robbery committed upon Widow Cordier at La Chapelle?"

"I should think so; and if I had my way, the robbers would be precious soon locked up."

"Well, if you like to take the matter in hand, and supply me with valuable information, I will reward you handsomely; and here are two five-franc pieces to begin your search with."

The woman went away enchanted, and came back three days later. This time she was shown in without any difficulty; but she was still half intoxicated, or perhaps a little more, for that was her habit.

"I have good news for you. One of my old friends had left her husband, because they were so badly off; and, as you know, when there is no hay in the manger the horses fight. But one fine morning they came together again. The husband bought her an entire wardrobe, which she wanted, for she was dressed much like myself; and they live in jollity every day, hardly ever leaving the wine-shop; and their friends declare that he did the trick for the widow with a man of the name of Toussaint, and an old fellow called Father Louis."

"What is the husband's name, and where does he live?"

"Wait a minute, and you shall see whether I am worthy to be a police-agent. His name is Lecalonec; and in order to know whether all I was told was true, I went to No. 24, Rue de Hambourg, where they lodge, as if pretending to pay a visit to the wife; but they were neither of them at home."

I thanked her for the information; and giving her ten more francs, sent her away, bidding her maintain the deepest secrecy. The next morning my principal inspector, Fraudin, accompanied by several agents, claimed the assistance of the police commissioner of the quarter and went with him to arrest Lecalonec, but the criminal managed to escape by a window. His accomplice, Toussaint, was arrested, however, and a sum of two thousand francs was found upon him; and shortly after Father Louis and Lecalonec were also in the hands of the police. At the house of the former fifteen hundred francs were seized, and about a thousand on the latter.

They were all then confronted with the Widow Cordier and young Dutertre, who recognised them by their voices, and described the part which each of them had played in the nocturnal drama. They were all three sentenced to penal servitude for life at the Assizes of October 25th, 1851. As we have seen, these criminals would probably have escaped scot-free if I had refused to see a creature who had fallen into the last stage of brutalization. When the question is to discover malefactors, no information should be despised, wherever it may come from; and it is frequently the lowest person who finds the trace of the criminal.

CHAPTER XXIII.

THE OFFICER'S WIFE.

With the rich as with the poor, life is only a romance, more or less long, more or less gay, whose dénouement is at times impressive. But in all these uncertain existences, among these romances of an hour or a day, according to the rarity or multiplicity of events, there is always one chapter, one agreeable or painful recollection by which the heart is affected, and which contains in itself frequently the interest of an entire life. With the ambitious man, it is the day on which, when he has succeeded in seeing his dream of pride or madness accomplished, he is suddenly supplanted by a rival, who suddenly destroys the result of a whole life of combinations, intrigues, and calculations. For the miser, it is the dreadful moment when the thief has stolen his treasure; with the young boarder, it is the hour when, delivered from the convent grate, after having long dreamed of the ideal and romantic love of some young man, she is suddenly thrown into the arms of an asthmatic old man or a brutal egotist. With nearly all, it is a disillusion of dreams caressed for a long time with delight—it is the deception brought into icy contact with reality.

Still, for some privileged persons, this unforeseen chapter has been marked by some great action, some glorious enterprise, some noble devotion : the latter form the minority, and it is not about one of these special existences that I wish to record emotions which leave an ineffaceable recollection. One day a lady of respectable age came to my office, accompanied by her daughter, Madame N———, who had been married for some years to an officer whose regiment was quartered in Paris. The saddened air of the mother, and even more the pallor and extreme despair marked on the daughter's face, which was remarkably beautiful, disposed me involuntarily to feel a compassion for which I did not know the cause.

"Sir," the mother said to me, "my daughter is resolved upon committing suicide; and she will certainly carry out this deplorable idea if you do not come to her assistance."

Two heavy tears, which had been for a long time restrained, ran silently down her thin cheeks.

"Good gracious, madame," I hastened to say to the young lady, "what can have happened to drive you to such an extremity?"

"Alas!" madame replied; "a precipice was before me—I allowed myself voluntarily to be led away, and if you can do nothing to save me, nothing is left me but death, for the tomb is preferable to the shame and infamy with which I am menaced."

"Be assured, madame, that I will do anything in my power to be useful to you."

"Thanks, sir! But I must tell you the whole truth, and I reckon on your indulgence to excuse the length of my story.

"I was eighteen years of age when my mother took me from the convent to live with her at a small town in the vicinity of Paris. As always happens, when a girl has a certain dowry, she has no want of offers; but I was young, and happy at the liberty I possessed. The world, which I scarce knew, seduced me, and left me too little time to think of marriage. I refused the offers made me, and my mother, who submitted to my wishes, and jealous of my happiness, approved of my resolution. This state of mind, habitual to girls, could not last for ever. Among the officers stationed in our town, and whom we met at times in society, I noticed one whose distinguished manners, noble and reserved air, and affable language, charmed me at first, and he soon captivated my heart. M. N—— asked for my hand: he pleased me—that was his best recommendation; and a short time after, my mother paid him over fifty thousand francs as my marriage portion.

"I was happy in the beginning of our union, and my husband was full of kindness to me. This happiness seemed as if it would never end; but, alas! my husband gradually displayed a cold indifference, and left me in a cruel isolation—cruel for me and dangerous for him. When he came home he was continually ill-tempered, and hardly addressed a word to me. This insupportable existence lasted for two years, during which I tried in vain to win him back to me by affectionate attentions and marks of love. Whenever I sought to reproach him with his indifference, and make him understand my heart-weariness, he would answer me, 'You are weary? Well, go and spend six or twelve months with your mother.' Wearied of seeing my advances so badly received, I resolved to write and tell all my sorrows to my mother, who urged me to follow my husband's advice, and come and join her. A few days later I was in her arms.

"A year passed away, during which my husband did not even express a wish for my return in the rare letters which he wrote me. I waited in vain for the summons, and then wrote to him that, if he wished it, I was ready to join him again; but he wrote me that this was impossible—that there was some talk of a change of quarters, and that we must save a double journey; but this was evidently a pretext. However this might be, I had but one thing to do, and that was, remain with my mother till my husband thought proper to recal me. While things were in this state, a friend of ours, to whom we were paying a visit, introduced to us a M. B——, adjutant of the regiment quartered in our town. He had a soft and insinuating voice, agreeable manners, a firm and assured glance, and was a very handsome man. He asked leave to pay his respects to us, and at first paid us a few rare visits, but gradually increased their frequency till he came to see us daily. I must have been blind not to see that he came solely for my sake : hence, one day when we were alone, he declared his love for me in passionate terms. I answered him in such a way as to leave him no hope ; and though he did not give up his schemes with reference to me, his visits became rarer, and I carefully avoided being alone with him.

"I had been living for eighteen months with my mother, when one morning I received a formal order from my husband to go and join him at V——, his new garrison town. When B—— learned that I was going away, he watched for a moment when my mother was out, and managed to make his way to the room in which I was sitting, without being previously announced. He began to talk to me again about his love : he was suppliant, and told me of his agony and tortures, but I repulsed him indignantly ; and when he saw that I would not swerve, he appeared in despair, and assumed a timid and respectful demeanour. He implored me to pardon him, and declared that, as he could not live without seeing me, he would make the most painful sacrifices to please me, and then went away.

"I will pass over my parting from my mother and my reception by my husband, who was still equally cold and indifferent. I frequently visited a friend of mine, our major's wife, in the hope of forgetting my sorrow; and one day, on going to call upon her, I met in the street a soldier, who bowed to me with some affectation. I looked at him, and noticed a great likeness to Adjutant B——, and thought that it might perhaps be his brother. The meeting greatly affected me; and the major's wife, on my joining her, noticed my trouble, and asked the cause of it.

"'It is a very trivial thing,' I replied. 'I have just met a private who bears an extraordinary likeness to a M. B——, an adjutant whom I met at times in society when I was living with my mother. This resemblance is so perfect, that I have not yet recovered from my surprise.'

"'Why, my dear child, the resemblance can be very easily explained. Adjutant B—— and the private whom you have just met are one and the same person. He is a sort of madman, an original, a mad-cap, who sent in his resignation in some regiment in order to join ours.'

"At these words I felt greatly troubled; for I remembered the oath which B—— had taken not to recoil before any sacrifice in rejoining me. I understood the meaning of his exchange; and pretending a violent headache, I at once asked permission to withdraw.

"On reaching my house, I went to bed in a high state of fever. During a long, sleepless night, I made disagreeable comparisons between my husband's conduct and that of M. B——. I established a dangerous parallel between the love of the one and the indifference of the other; between the devotion of the second and the coldness of the first; in short, shall I confess it to you, I was almost guilty, and I felt myself growing weak involuntarily. From this moment my visits to the officers' mess became more frequent; for each time that I went out I was certain of meeting B——, who very respectfully contented himself with bowing to me. Such respect could only make me esteem him, and I loved him already. One evening, on leaving my house, I met him face to face; and my surprise was so great that I could not decline taking a small note which he calmly offered me. I took the paper without knowing whether I was doing right or wrong, and went up to my room again. My husband was at the *café*, and would not come in till eleven. I opened the note, and it only contained these words: 'I implore you to grant me merely a glance.' This prayer, so full of humble resignation, pleaded better for him than any language could have done. At this moment the regiment received orders to change quarters. We were in the north, and received the route for the south, and thus had to cross the whole of France. My husband requested me to pass some time with my mother.

Such a request was an order for me, and I set off hurriedly, ere B—— could suspect my departure, and felt happy that my husband supplied me with such an easy mode of escape.

"I found my mother such as she had ever been to me,—that is to say, kind and affectionate. For a year I lived happily with her, when one day, to my misfortune, I saw B—— in an officer's uniform pass our windows. On the next day he called upon my mother as an old acquaintance, and I must confess that I saw him again with pleasure, for absence had not made me forget him. The Republic had given him his epaulettes again in a regiment quartered at Paris. Taking advantage of the way in which we received him, he repeated his visit; and ere long left the capital daily to come and spend several hours with us. I found him more amiable than ever. Our relations became more intimate; we exchanged letters, and I am sorry to say that this correspondence soon proved that he had nothing to desire beyond the constancy of my love. This state of things had been going on for six months, when I received a letter from my husband, informing me that his regiment was ordered to Paris. I had to choose between my lover and my husband; and I did not hesitate to break with the former. I was a mother; I had a child at boarding-school; and it was time for me to put an end to my guilty conduct. Moreover, I said to myself, B—— is an honourable man; he will understand my position : he loves me, and most assuredly will approve my resolution ; for if we have been fallible, there is still time to try and repair our error.

"But, how mistaken I was ! How badly had I judged the man whom I had loved so dearly, and for whom I had sacrificed maternal tenderness and conjugal duty ! When I told him of the determination I had formed of entirely breaking off our relations—when I tried to work upon that chord of honour in his heart which I thought so sensitive, he only answered me by an outburst of fury ; and protesting that I belonged to him, he swore that I should never return to my husband—if I attempted to do so, he knew how to prevent me. This language revolted me. My sin then appeared to me all the greater ; and I ordered B—— immediately to restore me the letters of mine which he held. He exclaimed with a wild accent that I should never have those letters ; that he would employ them to ruin me with my husband ; and that, in this way, when I was dishonoured in the sight of the world, and ignominiously expelled by my family, I should be only too glad to return to him. The last words aroused my indignation to the highest pitch, and without deigning to answer, I hurriedly left him. A few days after this scene, my husband arrived in Paris, where I at once joined him in apartments which he had taken near the barracks. I was scarce installed ere I learnt that B—— had sent in his papers, in order not to go to Corsica with his regiment; and two days after I received a letter by the post, in which he asked me to meet him, and threatened, in case of refusal, to make everything known to my husband.

"This letter remained unanswered. From this moment his rage was unbounded, and he went about everywhere telling all who cared to listen to him that I had been his mistress, and that he could prove it. At last he wrote to my husband, to tell him of our old relations, adding that he was ready to supply proofs of my adultery. After reading this letter, M. N—— handed it to me, saying—

"'Madame, if the crime of which you are accused be true, I will kill you, and then kill myself, in order not to be the laughing-stock of the army'

"This morning B—— wrote to him again, made an appointment for nine o'clock to-morrow at his lodgings, and offered to hand over to him the letters which he had received from me. Now, if my husband goes to this appointment, he will find me dead on his return! Such, sir, is the desperate position in which I find myself: see if you can withdraw me from it. My life is in your hands."

And her tears flowed abundantly.

I reassured her as well as I could. I promised her to find some mode of tearing from her persecutor the proofs which he possessed, and whose evidence would ruin her, and at the same time I recommended her to use every effort in her power to prevent her husband from going to the appointment before the hour indicated.

"Oh! I can promise that," she said. "He will not leave our house before nine o'clock."

This was all I wanted. I dismissed mother and daughter, after requesting them to come to me the next morning immediately after the husband's departure. I then proceeded to M. Carlier, and told him the whole affair, with its somewhat romantic details.

"B—— is a scoundrel," he said to me, "and even the woman recognises her fault, and is coming back to better feelings. We cannot reasonably allow a family to be broken up, and the future of a worthy officer compromised. Have you any means of saving them?"

"I can only see one—it is tearing the letters out of B——'s clutches. He is described as a political malcontent. I will send you in a report to that effect. You will then issue a search-warrant for arms, ammunition, or treasonable papers, and the deuce is in it if we do not contrive to get hold of these combustible letters."

"Yes, that is it. I consent; so make haste."

The next morning, at a very early hour, a search was made in B——'s room, and in addition to the papers that compromised himself, a packet was seized containing the whole of Madame N——'s correspondence. A few hours after, Madame N—— came into my office, accompanied by her mother. I handed the daughter the letters, and she fainted in an easy-chair. On recovering, a deep blush suffused her face—it was shame, repentance, and delight, which, however, was very legitimate. Yielding to her excitement, she threw her arms round my neck.

"Oh, sir," she said, "you have saved my life and my honour; for I had made all preparations for death on my return home, if this accursed correspondence were not in your hands."

The poor mother eagerly took her daughter home before the return of her husband, who, on reaching the meeting-place, learnt B——'s arrest, and returned convinced that he had had to deal with a scurvy impostor or a madman. As for Madame N——, she is now a good wife, patient with her husband, affectionate to her child, and kind and gentle to all. She is striving to expiate her faults by her exemplary behaviour.

CHAPTER XXIV.

SOMNAMBULISM.

For the last twenty years and more a new trade—a charlatanism which seduces man by its attraction to the marvellous—has attained a very great extension. Somnambulism is one more method among the great number already existing for working upon the good faith of credulous persons. All our newspapers have been frequently filled with puffs, in letters half an inch high, proclaiming Mlle. X—— or Mlle. G—— the most lucid somnambulist that ever appeared, and yet these puffs contained a frightful amount of falsehood, seduction, and deception! I do not attempt to discuss here the greater or less amount of lucidity of the mind under the influence of the magnetic sleep; but as regards the pretended miracles and phenomena so often taken advantage of by swindlers, I think it useful to mention several facts which will teach how much confidence ought to be granted to the somnambulist oracles.

A female came to my office one day, and told me that she was portress to a house near the Bourse, and that very morning, during a momentary absence, a bank note for one thousand francs and some other articles had been stolen from her table-drawer.

"And just imagine, sir," she continued, "that when I returned home I met on my door-step a young man who lives on the fifth floor of our house—a good-for-nothing scamp, who calls himself a lawyer's clerk out of work, who was pretending to be calm, though I feel sure that he was trembling with fear. At that moment I did not know anything; but when I discovered the robbery, I straightway called to mind my tenant's hang-dog look. I at once said to myself, 'I am certain he is the thief,' and then, as I do not like to act lightly, instead of making a disturbance, I went at once to a famous somnambulist, who said, while seeing me, though he was asleep, 'Well, you were robbed this morning by a young man who lives on the fifth floor of your house, who was formerly in an office, but is now doing nothing.' Then my somnambulist described everything there was in the thief's room, adding that the window faced the door. That was certainly an evident proof, and so I have come to ask you to arrest him at once and put him in prison. I have been to the police commissioner, but he refused to arrest the rascal and sent me to you."

"He acted rightly, madame, and you will permit me to tell you that I have so often been deceived by the statements of somnambulists that I set no faith in them."

"Still, sir, the somnambulist described him exactly before I mentioned my suspicions, and he described the room of the thief, though he has never seen it. There can be no doubt but that he has spoken the truth."

"Whatever you may say, I repeat that I am not allowed to arrest a man on such weak evidence. Watch your tenant; do not let him out of sight, so that he may be easily found when the moment arrives, and do not trouble yourself any more about the matter, as I shall take it in hand."

The portress went off greatly dissatisfied, saying that she did not understand why the police did not at once arrest a thief who was pointed out to them. I went to M. Carlier's office to speak to him about this affair.

"Very good," said the prefect; "but as ignorance at times renders people stupid, in order to prevent this good woman from declaring everywhere that the police are in a league with the thieves, I will issue a search-warrant, and thus prove that the lost objects are not in this young man's possession."

During this time the portress still went on. She had left my office in a fury; her walk heightened her agitation, and on reaching her house, she hastened to tell her neighbours of the result of her visit to the chief of the detectives. At this moment M. B——, a banker residing in the house, passed the lodge. He was a gossiping and very curious gentleman. The portress told him of the robbery and the revelations which the somnambulist had made to her. M. B——, amazed, wished to hear the supernatural revelation with his own ears, and ere long banker and portress proceeded side by side to the clairvoyant sleeper. The latter repeated the story which he had originally told the portress, and M. B——, more and more amazed, hurried to my office and wished to know why I had not arrested the individual suspected. One circumstance had wonderfully heightened the banker's faith; a list of names was handed to the somnambulist, in which that of the young clerk was purposely omitted, and he exclaimed, "Your thief is not in that, for his name is X——!"

Unfortunately for the convictions of the bankers and the portress, the search warrant was handed me at this very moment. I sent it off at once, and not the slightest trace of the stolen effects was found in X——'s room. Some time afterwards, and in consequence of delicate inquiries, suspicions rested on a portress in the same street; the house was searched, and it led not alone to the discovery of the articles stolen from the complainant, but also of some jewellery, filched from the same banker who accused me of arbitrary conduct when I did not have the young lawyer's clerk pointed out by the somnambulist arrested.

A girl of very respectable family of the name of Virginie disappeared from her parents' house, and a worthy magistrate, whom I had known for some time, made me an official report in the following terms :—

"Virginie is fair, young, and remarkably pretty; her character is wonderfully angelic, and it is impossible to exaggerate her personal charms. Moreover, she is a somnambulist, and possesses truly-astounding timidity. I have been present at several family experiments, in which she said so many surprising things, that if I had not heard them with my own ears I could not have believed them. Since her disappearance her parents have learned that whenever she went out, whether alone or with a servant—a gentleman, who was not exactly old or young, constantly followed her, and after accompanying her thus, did not leave her till she returned home. It is apprehended, not without reason, that this individual may have employed violence towards the young lady, in order to get her to a country house which he has at the village of B——, ten leagues from here. That which would seem to corroborate this alarm is, that he has not been seen again since Virginie's departure."

"Surely," I said, "a very simple way of making certain of this gentleman's culpability, is to send to that village some clever fellow, to learn whether the young lady is with him."

This was done, and the person entrusted with the affair declared that the suspected individual was quite alone at his country house. The parents, not knowing to what saint to appeal, now went to a somnambulist. He answered that their daughter had been carried off by a gentleman who had hired a room in a grocer's house in the Rue Compoise, at St. Denis; that at eleven o'clock the next morning, a porter of the name of C—— would be at the Porte St. Denis with a trunk; the ravisher would join him there, and the couple would have a hackney coach and proceed to join the young lady at St. Denis.

The worthy magistrate came to tell me of this oracle with such an air of conviction, that, out of politeness to him, I sent two agents to the Porte St. Denis, and two others to the Rue Compoise, with orders to arrest lover, mistress, and porter, and bring them to the prefecture. The former, after watching from 9 a.m. till 4 p.m., returned without seeing anybody, and their comrades very needlessly explored all the houses in the Rue Compoise. A few days after I saw the respectable magistrate again enter my office.

"Well," I asked him, "have you any news?"

"Yes, the young lady has returned to the paternal mansion."

"Ah, indeed! how so?"

"Well! some passers-by found her at La Villette, seated on the bank of the canal, with her feet hanging in the water. She was in a perfect state of somnambulism; and when she woke up she was taken home."

"But what had happened to her?"

"She is ignorant, and declares that she can remember nothing that occurred during her absence."

M. D——, a manufacturer of bronzes, living in the Marais, had a delightful country villa close to the gates of Paris, where he went every Sunday through the summer with his family, leaving his woman-servant to take charge of the shop and rooms. One day this guardianship proved inefficient, for his place was entered by means of false keys, and a considerable robbery was effected. On being informed of this occurrence, M. D—— at once returned home, and after making an investigation, was convinced that his servant had given her lover, a journeyman hatter, the means to commit the robbery. In spite of his conviction, he thought it his duty to consult a somnambulist, who confirmed his suspicions. Feeling now quite certain that he was not mistaken, he came to me and denounced his servant and the hatter, about whom I made inquiries, which proved most favourable. At the same time I had the hatter's room searched, but not one of the stolen articles was found. The affair ended here, and M. D—— was obliged to content himself with discharging his maid-servant, while remaining convinced that the robbery was committed at her instigation.

Six months later I learnt that a notorious robber was living in the Rue Traversière. I had him at once arrested, and in the search made at his domicile some knives were found bearing the trade mark of the bronze manufacturer. When questioned as to these articles, the convict declared that they were the proceeds of a robbery which he had committed by the aid of false keys, in the shop of a tradesman in the Marais. And yet the somnambulist had declared that the robbers were the maidservant and her lover!

I could quote at least fifty affairs, all alike with but slight variations; but what should I prove? That somnambulism, so far as concerns the prediction of the future and the revelation of things unknown, is, as I stated at the outset, a trade, a charlatanism, and that the somnambulist, like the flatterer in the fable, lives at the expense of the person who listens to him; but this is, I think, sufficiently demonstrated. At that period magnetism was not merely fashionable, but was a fury, a rage. The smallest meeting of friends must have its somnambulist experimenting, and it was an epidemic!

In the porter's lodge, in the student's garret, in the banker's drawing-room, everybody indulged in studies of second sight; all wished to be lucid; and all over Paris there were only somnambulists, magnetizers, and credulous proselytes; in this way was prepared the reign of turning hats, speaking tables, and rapping spirits.

Naturally, the confidence in a quasi-supernatural

power led all the persons who suffered from a robbery to have recourse to somnambulism in order to discover the thieves. Now all, or nearly all, presented themselves to this oracle of a new description, with a fixed idea of suspicion directed to an individual. So soon as a robbery is committed in a house, the person robbed does not fail to suspect a lodger, or one of the servants, in consequence of the reasoning, that in order to plunder a suite of rooms the thieves must be acquainted with the habits of the man who occupies them, in order to take advantage of his absence to commit the crime. But how can such doubts be exclusive when we are aware of the behaviour of the professional burglar, who plans an affair for several months beforehand, and that one of them does not take his eyes off the victim, so that he may warn the thieves of the unexpected return of the lodger! Or, take again the case of a daring thief, a Renaud for instance, who taps softly at a door, then taps louder, and lastly, on receiving no answer, opens the door with a false key, and after carrying off everything that is in them, goes off as noiselessly as he has come.

Hence, nearly all these poor people, victims of more or less adroit robbers, came to lay siege to me, and I was daily compelled to listen to depositions, all referring to robberies of a more or less important nature, and indicating the name and address of the robber, dictated by the somnambulist. Daily, after receiving these charges, I was compelled to disillusionize the complainants, which was not always easy, and send them away excessively dissatisfied, for they had come with the settled conviction that the police only needed to lay hands upon the malefactors who were so explicitly pointed out to them.

CHAPTER XXV.

A POISONING CASE.

It is a remarkable fact, that nearly all the actions which society reproves, and accordingly condemns, bear their own punishment within themselves, and what strikes me most is, that the chastisement assails three-fourths of the individuals who habitually frequent houses of prostitution. One man is wounded, another is beaten, another falls ill, another, again, ruins his health and purse; lastly, others find death there owing to circumstances beyond all foresight, and which seem to be terrible warnings given by Providence in order to keep persons from frequenting these infamous places.

Before I narrate an instance, all the details of which I was in a position to know, I will mention here the death of that National Guard who, instead of tranquilly mounting guard and returning home respectably, spent the night at Grognard's licensed house in the Rue de la Tannerie, and was killed by the sudden fall of that house of debauchery. May the recollections of that catastrophe, and of the following fact, produce a salutary restraint upon those who are inclined to haunt such houses!

On December 31st, 1849, at about five in the morning, a porter came to a prostitute of the name of Vher, who lived in the Rue de la Victoire, and handed her a small box containing six cakes covered with cream, which a stranger had requested him to deliver to her. This box, so sent, was too like an act of gallantry to be refused; Mademoiselle Vher attributed the attention to some adorer of yesterday, to-day, or even to-morrow, and shared the cakes with her maid-servant; but half an hour had scarce elapsed from eating, when the life of both was in danger; the cakes had been sprinkled with arsenic. At eight o'clock on the same evening, a porter also went to the tolerated house, No. 3, Rue de Vert Bois, and handed one Louise Ronceaux a glass box, containing five little cream cakes, and a letter signed Sophie Ronceaux, her sister, announcing the sending of this box. At one in the morning, after the girls had supped, this Louise shared her cakes with several of her companions, and one T——, an enameller, who was in the house at the time. Almost immediately after, all were attacked by a frightful cholera. T——, as well as one Mademoiselle Griffon, expired on the same night.

The similitude of these crimes, the circumstances which preceded them, and the sufferings that resulted, perfectly proved that one and the same hand had simultaneously distributed the poison. The private relatives of the two girls soon pointed out the culprit. For many years a man of the name of Jean Claude Aymès, a very clever copper-plate engraver, had preferred to live on the disgraceful prostitution of Mademoiselle Vher, and then upon that of Mademoiselle Ronceaux. The latter was hardly sixteen years of age, when she was seduced and taken from her family by Aymès, who brought her to Paris to place her in a brothel. These two creatures, tired of Aymès' ill-treatment, had in turn resolved to leave him, and, although he had threatened to poison them, they refused to renew their relations with him.

The information obtained soon converted these probabilities into certainties. The porter who delivered the last box declared that it was given him by a young man of the name of Provo, whose address he gave. The latter declared, in his turn, that this box had been given him by a man whom he did not know, who ordered him to hand it to the porter standing at the corner of the Rue St. Denis. At length Aymès was arrested, sentenced to death and executed.

On the day of the double poisoning, T——, the enameller, was conveyed home, and, as I stated, he died during the course of the day. A workman, who had been in his service for a short time, of the name of Gaillard, offered to the widow to sit up with the body, and this offer was gratefully accepted, so gratefully, indeed, that, with the help of the devil, a month later Gaillard was publicly known as the happy lover of the inconsolable widow.

This Gaillard had been tried several times for robbery and forgery, and on the last occasion was sentenced to four years' imprisonment and surveillance. Physically, Gaillard was a handsome man, in the full meaning of the term; he was tall and well built, he had a white and red complexion and large blue expressive eyes, his long hair was black and silky, while thick moustaches imparted a masculine and resolute expression to his face. These advantages the Widow T——, who was anything but pretty, had appreciated only too well, and as I have stated she soon yielded to the amorous pressing of the journeyman. Still, let me hasten to add that marriage was eventually to consecrate their guilty relations; but an unforeseen obstacle sprang up between the two lovers, and separated them for ever. One day Widow T—— received a letter, denouncing Gaillard as a convict placed under surveillance; and after reading this unlucky letter, a violent scene took place. Gaillard energetically denied the truth of the letter, and broke into such imprecations and threats of death against the unknown author, that his mistress, greatly alarmed, ran away, with the determination to discover whether what was written about her lover were true. In that case she was resolved to break with him for good. In order to enlighten herself on this point she came to me, and begged me to let her know whether Gaillard was a convict standing under police surveillance.

"Madame, I cannot answer your question."

"But, here, sir, is a letter which I have just received, and you alone can tell me whether the statements it contains are true."

"Certainly; but I cannot, and must not reveal to any person the judicial position of another party."

"In that case, sir, although the police are aware that a man has been to the galleys, they would allow him to marry a respectable girl and cheat an honest family, sooner than make his position known! I consider that infamous."

"To all that, madame, I can only give one answer, that the police can inform the judges alone of the antecedents of individuals. As for those families that desire a certainty about suspicions which they may entertain, a file of the *Gazette des Tribunaux* is at their service at all the reading rooms, and so they can easily remove their doubts."

Knowing the judicial position of Gaillard, but unable to divulge it, I resolved on this evasive answer in order at once to offer a safety plank to the unfortunate woman. Widow T—— replied with considerable animation, that although she could obtain no information from the police, she was resolved to obtain, at any cost, the positive information which she desired, and that she would know no rest till she had done so. "For," she added, "I swear by Heaven that if Gaillard is under surveillance, I will break off all relations with him, and never see him again." On leaving my office she proceeded to the Palace of Justice, and picked up one of the old public writers; placing twenty francs in his hand, she requested him to make the requisite search, promising him a handsome reward if, within two days, he gave her the information which she had such interest in obtaining. The old scribe, who was well versed in all assize matters, was speedily enabled to lay before his generous client the newspaper containing the report of Gaillard's trial.

I was unaware of these facts when, a fortnight after the visit which widow T—— had paid me, she came to me once again, informed me of the steps which she had taken to enlighten herself, and concluded by begging me to protect her against the fury of her ex-lover. The scenes of separation had been terrible. Gaillard had gone away vomiting curses and threats upon his mistress; but he had not given any expression to his anger, until he learnt that the Widow T—— had resolved to secure a protector, by marrying one C——. On hearing this, Gaillard in his fury, called on the widow, and swore to kill her unless she broke off the match and consented to marry him.

I sent for Gaillard, and ordered him very sternly to

leave the Widow T—— at peace, threatening, if he did not do so, to have him expelled from Paris, and Gaillard promised to obey my instructions. For several months I heard nothing about either party. In the following January, Madame T—— called on me again to protect her against Gaillard, who had threatened on several occasions to assassinate her. I ordered chief inspector Fraudin, who knew both Gaillard and the widow well, to set two agents on the watch to protect the woman, and I looked about for Gaillard, though in vain, as he was hiding under a false name. The affair remained in this state until towards the middle of February, 1851. The Widow T—— came to my office again, though this time to thank me for my kindness, and to ask me, as she had heard no more of Gaillard, to discontinue my surveillance of her premises. I acquiesced in her request, while feeling a sort of apprehension that what I feared would be realized, and though I recalled my agents, I requested Sergeant Fraudin to call every now and then at the widow's, to make sure that she was not disquieted.

Unhappily, what I foresaw occurred. Gaillard, who, in fear of being arrested, had prudently kept in hiding so long as the watch had lasted, suddenly reappeared when it ceased, and learning that his ex-mistress was on the eve of marrying her new lover, he resolved to kill her before the wedding had taken place. On Feb. 27, he presented himself at the domicile of the

Widow T——, in the Rue Phillipeaux, and without reproaching her, uttering the slightest threat, or even speaking to her, he fired two pistol shots at her, and attempted to escape. But at the moment when his victim was expiring, the neighbours, terrified by the double discharge, closed the gates, and the murderer, thus caught in a trap, was speedily handed over to the authorities. When examined, Gaillard declared that he had committed the crime with premeditation; but in spite of his positive and detailed confession, the jury with a degree of indulgence which other, and less guilty, men have not always met with, threw out the aggravating fact of premeditation, and Gaillard was condemned to penal servitude for life.

Impelled to commit this crime by the irregular passion with which a woman who had nothing seductive about her, inspired him, Gaillard had become an assassin through love. Before committing the crime he had made several attempts to meet Fraudin, and blow out his brains, because he was persuaded that the loss of his mistress, and her resolution of marrying another man, were owing to the insinuations of my chief inspector. Hence, on leaving la Roquette to be conveyed to Brest, he swore that he would escape from the hulks and return to Paris to murder Fraudin, the presumed author of all his misfortunes. During his detention at Mazas, this man, who only dreamed of blood and vengeance, employed his days in making crowns, which he sent porters to lay on the tomb of his victim at Père la Chaise.

Two years elapsed after these events. Fraudin, after laughing at Gaillard's threats, eventually forgot them completely, till it was told us that the murderer of Widow T—— had escaped from the galleys, as he had declared. No one knew what had become of him, but he must be certainly on the road for Paris, as he had sworn to assassinate Fraudin, and would do it. In this man, vengeance was all in all; and we have seen him at work. In fact, he proceeded to the capital, and reached his destination on the twentieth day after his escape. He all but held the realization of his desire:—he was in the same city as the man whom he pursued with his implacable vengeance, any moment might bring them face to face, and one must die—we can guess which, for in a struggle between an armed assassin and an honest man without defence, the result cannot be doubtful. But the hand of Heaven guided Gaillard to the Rue St. Lazare; enough blood had been shed by this villain, and his crimes were counted. He met here a comrade, and both turned into a wine-shop, where they indulged in copious libations: their heads grew hot, and Gaillard told his chum all the details of his escape; but the master of the house overheard the whole conversation. When midnight arrived, the wine-dealer left his waiter to shut up the house, and prudently followed Gaillard at a distance, to learn where he lived. At five o'clock the next morning the police commissioner of the quarter, warned by the honest tradesman, went to the indicated house, and the escaped convict, found in bed, was sent back to the hulks with a powerful escort. Fraudin only owed his life to this providential circumstance.

CHAPTER XXVI.

THE FRAUDULENT BANKRUPT.

M. B——, an intimate friend of the prefect of police, came to tell him one morning that one K——, a merchant, whose creditor he was to the extent of seventy thousand francs, had just filed his schedule, but it was a fraud.

"The rogue is in hiding," said M. B——; "but if he could be got hold of, I would undertake to make him disgorge."

M. Carlier sent the complainant to me, and requested me to make every exertion in finding this honest bankrupt. M. B—— told me that his debtor lived, prior to his disappearance, on the St. Martin Boulevard, and this was all the information he could give me. I went, myself, to make inquiries at the house indicated. I learnt that M. K——'s apartments were still occupied by his wife, but that for the moment he was out of town. The truth was that, since the day of his flight, he had not once returned home. As I fancied that pressing my inquiries might compromise the success of the affair, I went away. On the other hand, I learned from a porter that M. K—— had several times given him letters to carry to a woman whom he kept in the Rue du Faubourg Montmartre. I established a surveillance at the house of the latter, as well as at that of the wife. The agents had orders to arrest K—— if he presented himself at either of these houses, and to follow the two females wherever they might go; and, as they went out in hackney coaches, I placed a hired cabriolet at the service of each watcher. All these measures led to no result; and during a week that my agents remained on the watch, from six in the morning till midnight, nothing revealed what we wished to know, namely, the residence of the bankrupt.

Everybody knows that postmen are accustomed to call aloud, at the door of the porters' lodges, the names of the inmates to whom letters are addressed. I therefore had the postman followed by an agent, sufficiently near for the latter to hear the names pronounced; and in the event of there being a letter for either of the females the agent would at once enter the lodge, get into conversation with the porter under some pretext, and try to discover the post-mark of the town whence the letter came. This plan failed, like all the rest; and a few days later the inspector ordered to follow the postman at Madame K——'s house could not refrain from saying, as he made his report—

"That old porter is as obstinate as the real Picard

he is!—his tenant must have bribed him handsomely."

The fact is that, up to the present, we had had to deal with a tough adversary; and whatever the schemes we employed, they remained unsuccessful. One word, however, struck me.

"Do you say that he is a Picard?"

"Yes, sir."

"What makes you think so?"

"Oh, it is easy to recognise that through his accent."

"Very good," I remarked; "in that case we shall probably get hold of our man."

I at once sent for one of my irregular Cossacks, who, having worked for a long time in different towns of Picardy, was perfectly acquainted with the dialect, and could very easily pass himself off as a full-blooded Picard. I explained the position to him clearly, and concluded—

"You will go to the porter at Madame K——'s house, and in order to get into conversation, ask for the first person whose name occurs to you. He will reply that he does not know anyone of that name, and hence will result a little explanation, which you will end by suddenly exclaiming, 'Bless me, you are a Picard!' The man will reply in the affirmative; and you, as a countryman of his, will offer him a glass of wine at the nearest bar. But, instead of that, you are to be careful to sit down with him over a bottle of good wine. This you will have succeeded by another, until you find your porter on the point of becoming confiding and loquacious. You will then tell him, under the seal of secresy, that you have been in business, that things went bad, and that the police are after you, but that you have managed to foil all their schemes. This confession, made in your quality as a Picard, will surely provoke that of your companion; and as your position is identical with that of K——, he will probably tell you in his turn the story of his lodger, perhaps without mentioning his name, but most certainly with such precision that we shall be able to find him."

My Cossack was an intelligent fellow: he played his part admirably; and matters occurring exactly as I had foreseen, we learnt that our bankrupt was in hiding at Montmartre, under the unpretending name of M. André. But here a fresh difficulty presented itself. K—— lived in a room whose windows opened on a garden, in which was a door leading to a back lane. At the slightest alarm, he could, therefore, take to flight, and, moreover, he frequently slept out. On the next day, I sent to Montmartre three agents, one of whom only was to enter the house. He was disguised as a mail-guard, and bore a book and a bag containing eight hundred francs in silver. According to my instructions, he went to the porter.

"Does M. André live here?"

"Yes; but he is out."

"That is a nuisance. I have brought him eight hundred francs sent him from Bordeaux" (and while saying this he shook the bag), "and I really cannot come such a long distance again."

"Good gracious!" the porter muttered. "I really do not know what to do. M. André has strictly ordered me not to tell any one—no matter who—where he is."

"That is possible, old fellow," the agent answered. "Your M. André, from what I can see, has probably creditors, and does not want them to know where he is. That is all very well; but it is no reason to keep out of the way of persons who bring you money. Still——"

"That is true, on my word," the porter remarked, flattered by this argument, which he could understand. "People who bring money are more respected. Well, sir, since that is the case, M. André goes every morning to the office of a M. Z——, in the Rue St. Denis, and you will find him there."

The agent set off at once, but he said to himself, "K—— is a sharp fellow, who distrusts everything, and who seems to guess the plans made to arrest him. If I were to go and stupidly ask for M. André, he is capable of sending some one to answer in his name, and slip through our fingers on finding that it is merely an excuse to nail him." Under the influence of these reflections, the pretended guard, followed at a distance by the other two agents, reached the Rue St. Denis, and asked the house-porter to be good enough to show him in to M. André, that he might hand him a bag of money which he had for him.

The porter hastily introduced my agent into one of M. Z——'s offices, and addressing the person in it, said to him—

"M. André, here is a mail-guard who has a bag of money to deliver to you."

But to the great amazement of the porter, as well as the equal stupefaction of M. K——, the false guard had already laid his hand on the bankrupt's shoulder, saying—

"M. K——, I have a warrant to arrest you."

K——, escaping from the clutch of the agent, as if it were a red-hot iron, took up his hat, and, while making some remarks, was preparing for a fresh flight; but at this moment the other two agents entered the office, and, judging any resistance useless, he allowed himself to be quietly led to the Prefecture. As for M. B——, the Prefect's friend, I never learnt whether, through this arrest, he was enabled to recover his 70,000 francs, as he had stated.

CHAPTER XXVII.

LEON LAMBEL AND LESPINASSE.

In the month of August, 1849, a considerable robbery was effected to the prejudice of Mlle. H——, actress at the Théâtre Historique. Audacious thieves, taking advantage of her compulsory absence at the theatre, entered her rooms by the help of false keys, broke open the drawers, and went off with the most valuable articles. On being informed of the burglary, I proceeded to the spot. When I had the circumstances connected with it explained to me, I learnt that in one room, a little horse of oxidised silver, minus half one leg, and which had been apparently detached from a swell-mobsman's watch-chain, had been picked up. I carefully examined the traces of the burglary, and did not hesitate for a moment in declaring to the persons present, that, in my opinion, there were only two men in Paris, Léon Lambel and Lespinasse, both liberated convicts, capable of performing a robbery under such conditions, and with as much daring as skill. A literary man, who had come through curiosity, with some of the actors, to inquire into the details of the robbery, looked at me with the greatest astonishment.

"What!" he said to me, "you can guess the perpetrators of a robbery by merely seeing in what way it was committed? It is truly marvellous, and if you can furnish me with proofs that these two men are the robbers, I promise to give a column to your skill in a newspaper."

"Oh," I answered him, "it is not worth the trouble, though I am obliged to you. Still I am anxious to prove to you that I know the thieves, and ere long I hope to show that no doubt is possible as to the guilt of my two convicts."

From that day, Léon Lambel and Lespinasse became the objects of the most active and persevering search. Unfortunately I was destined to experience the greatest difficulty in discovering them; for only one of my agents, Sallen, and myself, knew Lambel, because we had arrested him on the Boulevard when I was a peace-officer. On the other hand, I had no positive proofs against the two men, only my own conviction, and I could not expect that others would share it with me. I therefore required other arguments to impress my charge, and enable me to go straight to my proposed point. For this purpose I summoned my Cossack irregulars to the office.

"Are there any among you," I asked, "who were at

the Brest galleys, and knew Léon Lambel and Lespinasse, but the former more especially?"

"I—I—I, sir."

"Is it long since you saw him?" I asked the first.

"At least a year."

"And you?"

"Oh, a good six months."

"And you?" I asked the third.

"I saw him about two months back. I met him in the Faubourg du Temple, and the proof is, that we drank a pint of wine at the shop at the corner of the Rue Mericourt."

"Was any one with him?"

"No; he was alone."

"How was he dressed?"

"Oh, like a regular swell! Black frock coat and trousers, and patent leather boots."

"But did he wear any jewellery, diamond studs, or a watch?"

"Yes, he had a watch, for I remember my wife, La Pucelle, saying to him, 'Give me that little toy at the end of your watch-chain.' He refused, and so La Pucelle said, in her turn, 'Why, your horse is not so very grand, for he has a broken leg."

"A broken leg!"

"Oh, I mean one half was missing."

"Then you noticed this ornament particularly?"

"Certainly I did."

"Where is the Pucelle at this moment?"

"She is doing six months at St. Lazare."

"Ah, indeed; thank you. And now," I added, addressing them collectively; "you can be off, and if you meet Lambel and Lespinasse, pick a quarrel with them, so that you may be all arrested together, and brought here as convicts who have broken their ban. I pledge myself to set you at liberty directly, and give you one hundred francs as a recompence. Be off!" and my Cossacks left me, determined to let themselves be torn piecemeal, sooner than miss so fine a chance. Immediately after they had left me, I took a cab and went to St. Lazare, where I ordered La Pucelle to be brought before me. I asked her the following questions without further preface:—

"How long are you imprisoned for?"

"For six months."

"Well, if you will be frank and tell me the whole truth about what I am going to ask you, I will have you let out to-morrow."

"Make haste and speak."

"Is it long since you saw Léon Lambel?"

"About two months. I was with my man. We met him in the Faubourg du Temple, and he paid for some wine."

"Had he any jewellery on when you met him?"

"Yes; he had rings, a watch and chain, and among his trinkets was a small horse that looked like silver and wanted a foot. I asked him to give it to me, and he refused."

"Well, do you know this?" and at the same time I showed her the trinket found on Mdlle. H——.

"Why, that is Lambel's toy; I recognise it perfectly."

I broke off my questioning; but on the next day the Pucelle was free, as I had promised her.

I must confess that I felt the greatest satisfaction on seeing my convictions confirmed by this evidence, for they had hitherto been merely a presumption.

About this time M. Peloile, a wine-dealer at No. 3, Rue d'Italie, came to inform me that two persons, who had breakfasted in a room on his first floor, had entered his private rooms and stolen a sum of six thousand seven hundred and ten francs, of which four thousand were in notes and the rest in cash, and also a silver cup, a watch, and a pistol. I asked him for a description of the two men, and at once recognised Léon Lambel and Lespinasse. I then inquired into all the circumstances, and sent away the wine-dealer, telling him that I would send for him and his waiter, to confront them with the robbers so soon as the latter were arrested. Still I had further vexations to undergo; for some days I had completely lost all traces of my culprits, and like a miner whose lamp has suddenly gone out in a subterranean gallery, I advanced with hesitation and groping my way. But Lambel and his accomplice undertook to provide the clue which led to their lurking-place. A fresh robbery committed by them in the Rue Saint Lazare enabled me to carry on my search more effectually.

Léon Lambel was first met at Monceaux by a person unconnected with the police; then an active surveillance carried on by four agents led at last to the discovery that their comrades and their mistresses lived in an isolated house near the Monceaux barrier. It was midnight when the four agents posted themselves round the house. I had given them orders to watch the approaches, and not enter till daybreak, for the purpose of arresting the robbers. At about two in the morning the street-door noiselessly opened. Léon Lambel and Lespinasse appeared on the threshold; but ere the agents could rush upon them, they drew bayonet pistols and disappeared in the darkness. An agent standing at the end of the street, seeing the two robbers, ran towards them and ordered them to surrender, but they pointed their pistols at him, saying, "Yes, we are the men you are looking for, but here is an answer for you." Unintimidated by this threat, the agent armed himself in his turn, and continued to pursue them. Unluckily, in this deserted quarter night concealed the two villains, who soon disappeared entirely.

While this scene was taking place at the end of the street, a woman came out of the house and was arrested by my agents; it was Maria F——, Lespinasse's mistress. In the basket she was carrying were found a bundle of twenty-four false keys, an assortment of files, a small vice, and other housebreaking tools, three crucibles still warm, and a lump of gold produced by melting down Mdlle. H——'s jewellery. The search made in the house led to the discovery of most of the articles stolen from the actress, such as dresses, lace, shawls, earrings, stockings in which Mdlle. H——'s name had been woven in the loom, as well as a silver mounted sugar-basin and other articles stolen from M. Grégoire. Maria F—— was tried at the assizes, and sentenced to ten years' hard labour.

In the following month of May I learned that Lespinasse was in the Rue de Courcelles, and I accordingly sent two agents and a sergeant at daybreak to arrest him. According to the instructions which I had given them, they went straight up to the door of his room and knocked, but received no answer. One of them, who stooped down and looked through the keyhole, saw the robber feeling in his great-coat pocket. In less than an instant the door was burst in by the agents; Lespinasse seized, and the coat torn from his grasp, in the pockets were found two pistols loaded to the muzzle. When questioned as to the use he intended to make of them, the convict replied that if time had been allowed him he would have infallibly blown out the brains of the first agent who entered.

In his room were found a dozen new false keys to open front doors, as well as a considerable sum of money.

This is the right place, I think, to say a word about the formidable partnership between Lambel and Lespinasse. Lespinasse was tall, possessed herculean strength, and a savageness which almost reduced him to a state of nature. His was the ferocious character of the savage, corrupted by the wants which civilization had created. As he always went out armed, he was constantly ready to help in a robbery, or protect his retreat by murder. While Lespinasse offered the perfect type of ignorance joined to cupidity and the coldest cruelty, Léon Lambel, who was young, elegant, and insinuating, was a specimen of the fashionable robber, who only worked in yellow kid gloves and patent leather boots. With these manifold advantages, Lambel easily entered the best houses and the most select society, and obtaining there all necessary information with a tact which removed the slightest shade of suspicion, it was easy for him to ripen his plans at his leisure, and only attempt a stroke when he was certain of success. In a word, in the union of two formidable and vitiated beings, Lambel was the soul, the head that conceived, arranged, and prepared matters, while Lespinasse was the strong, clever arm that carried them out. Lespinasse was brought to my office immediately upon his arrest, and I spoke to him about the robbery committed upon Mademoiselle H——.

"I cannot deny it," he said; "as you found in my room various objects connected with that robbery."

"You were in that other affair, too."

"Which one?"

"Why, the 6700 francs which you stole from the eating-house at the Barrière d'Italie."

"I do not know what you mean."

"What! Do you pretend to be ignorant of that robbery?"

"Perfectly."

"In that case it is different; we will look into that afterwards."

"I shall give you the same answer then as now."

"Very good, so we will say no more about it; but if you will tell me what you did with Mademoiselle H——'s cashmere shawl, or where I can find it, I promise to give you some comforts in prison."

"Oh, that's it? do you expect me to say anything! Well, thank you, you can wait for a long time, *as I am not hungry, and do not feel inclined to eat* (denounce)."

On the next day, working upon probably the only feeling which Lespinasse possessed, a sincere affection for his two sisters, most respectable girls, I sent for them to beg them to induce their brother to make revelations; and then I had him brought from his cell. As I hoped, the sight of the two girls affected the convict most deeply. Weeping like a child, he rushed into their arms, and held them in a long embrace; but at the first word they said about revelations, his natural ferocity regained the mastery, and he again became the suspicious, brutal, and insolent convict. In vain did his sisters and myself do all in our power to learn where the shawl was, he detected all our schemes, rejected all our entreaties, and resisted all our offers. I learned afterwards that he only acted thus because the shawl was in the possession of Léon Lambel's mistress.

Pursuing my investigations, I sent for the robbed wine-dealer and his waiter. I told the former that one of the men who plundered him was arrested, and on my showing him the two pistols found upon Lespinasse, he at once recognised one of them as his.

"Now," I said to him, "you and your waiter must be confronted with your robber."

Lespinasse was brought in and at once recognised, and he did not hesitate any longer to avow that the robbery had been effected by himself in complicity with Lambel.

While this affair was being investigated, we at length managed to get hold of a woman who called herself Noël, alias the Widow Bernard, who was charged with stealing 1400 francs from a Dr. Duvivier, to whom she was servant, and another robbery committed upon a Madame St. Aubin, whom she had been servant with under another name. She was at once brought to my office, and her face displayed an assurance and calmness, which to me evidenced all the greater perversity.

"It was you who committed the robbery in the Rue de Trevise?"

"What robbery, sir?"

"The one upon your late mistress, Madame de St. Albin."

"I will take my oath that I do not know the lady, and do not understand what you mean."

"Your protestations are useless; and it was not your maiden attempt, for you are terribly hardened in crime."

"I, sir! You are certainly mistaken."

"Stay! you say that your name is Widow Bernard. I would make a heavy bet that this is not your name."

"What would you have me call myself?"

"I do not know, but it will not be difficult to learn. I will have you taken first to St. Lazare, and if you are not known there, I will send you to Clermont prison, where you are certain to be recognised."

"If that is the case, sir, I will save you the trouble, for I see that I shall gain nothing by hiding myself any longer. My real name is Pallery. I have been convicted several times, the severest sentence being in

1839, when I was sentenced to ten years' penal servitude and surveillance. I confess that I robbed Dr. Duvivier and Madame St. Albin, but I was not alone in the affair, and the robberies were committed under the following circumstances. One evening, on leaving the Ambigu Theatre, I met Lambel, whom I knew to be a liberated convict and professional thief. We conversed and—well, I passed the night with him. I then promised to put him up to a robbery at my master's, and, taking advantage of his absence, I introduced Lambel into his apartments. His friend Lespinasse kept watch in the street, and when all was finished I disappeared with Lambel. A few days after this affair I obtained a situation with Madame Saint Albin. I told Lambel; he committed the robbery, and I went off with him again. This is the exact truth."

In consequence of these facts, Lespinasse and Mlle. Pallery were tried, and sentenced as relapsed convicts each to twenty years' penal servitude. But, during this time, what was Léon Lambel about? After Lespinasse's arrest he found his younger brother, Jules, also a liberated convict, and they left Paris to get out of the way of the police. They proceeded to Nantes, got into a jeweller's shop by raising the cellar flap, and escaped with 30,000 francs' worth of jewels. After this master stroke, the pair proceeded to Turin, where they committed a fresh robbery of 80,000 francs. We see that they were not idle.

But in March, 1854, the chief detective of Geneva was informed by a goldsmith in that city, that two Frenchmen, who called themselves commercial travellers, had ordered two of those silver cases called *bastringues*. This requires a short explanation. The bastringue is exclusively employed by robbers; this instrument, which is of very small dimensions, contains small watch-spring saws, a pair of false moustaches, and a few other articles very useful in assuring the success of an escape. It is concealed in a certain part of the body which I cannot name, and derives its name from the noise it produces when the robber begins running.

The chief of the Geneva police had agents posted near the goldsmith's house, and when the two men came to fetch their cases they were arrested, and efforts made to prove their identity. Informed of this arrest and perceiving that Léon Lambel might very possibly be one of the prisoners, the French police thought it as well to send an agent to make sure of the fact. Sallier, who besides myself was the only one who knew the ex-convict, was intrusted with this duty, the result of which was the transference of the artful robber to Paris. On August 29th of the same year, he was tried at the assizes and sentenced to twenty years' penal servitude for the robbery effected upon Mdlle H——.

CHAPTER XXVIII.

A DANGEROUS INTRIGUE.

ONE day, a lady of very remarkable beauty entered my office, and asked for a moment's interview. She was an adorable creature; I think the prettiest woman I ever saw in my life.

"How can I be of service to you, madame?"

At these words my charming visitor suffered from a momentary embarrassment, but quickly recovering herself, she said:—

"The circumstances which have brought me require entire confidence, and so I will tell you the whole truth."

"My name is Madame Z——. My husband, who is a respectable and respected merchant, possesses a fine fortune, and during the two years I have borne his name, I am bound to confess that he has always shown me the most assiduous and tender attention. Unfortunately his excessive love and kindness have contracted all my sorrow, all my grief, all my misfortunes, and all my faults, I am forced to add. Last year, wishing to procure me the largest amount of pleasure possible, he sent me to spend the summer with my mother, who has a country-house in the vicinity of X——. You are aware that in the country proximity is a sufficient reason for intimacy, and near my mother's house resided a very rich lady, descended from one of the first families in France. Her only son, an officer in a cavalry regiment, had come to spend a two months' furlough with her. Young, handsome, noble, skilled in all manly exercises, attractive in conversation, and well educated, Ernest (such was the young man's name) possessed all the necessary qualifications to be beloved, and as our families met daily, I soon noticed his continued attentions to myself. If his lips had never uttered a word of love in my ear, his eyes, full of fire, had often expressed it. Still, I must confess that, through a levity which was more inconsiderate than culpable, I at first made a sport of this love. Flattered by the passion which I had inspired, and withal fearing the consequences, I took a pleasure in stimulating this passion, and then my coquettishness urged me to take every possible opportunity to excite his jealousy. One circumstance soon raised this jealousy to its highest pitch. On my mother's birthday, my husband came from Paris to spend three happy days with me, like a schoolboy enjoying his holidays. At the time when he arrived, Ernest and his mother were at our house, and he was introduced to them. My husband thanked them for their politeness in rendering my stay in the country so agreeable.

"While these few remarks were being exchanged, I attentively examined Ernest; he had so changed that his mother noticed his pallor as well, and asked him were he ill? 'No, mother,' he answered; 'but I have just been suddenly attacked by a frightful headache, and I ask the permission of these ladies to retire.'

"My mother's birthday passed very sadly. Ernest did not reappear at our house, and when we sent to ask after him, we heard that he was a little better, but unable to leave his room. This sudden illness did not seem to me very natural, and I could understand the cause of it. Ernest did not make his appearance again during the three days my husband spent in the country. M. Z——, whom business recalled to the capital, left us, and in the evening Ernest and his mother came to invite us to dinner on the next day.

"After, dinner, it was proposed that we should stroll about a wood near the house, and, as usual, Ernest offered me his arm. Our mothers followed, but slowly, as persons walk at their age. Talking about one thing and the other, we were soon considerably ahead, and then Ernest spoke to me for the first time about his love: he confessed that his illness was only the jealousy he felt at the sight of my husband, and he described to me his sorrows and sleepless nights. I listened, but no longer with my usual indifference, but with pleasure. He became pressing. I had to answer him; but I foresaw that my senses were leaving me. In my terror I turned as if to summon my mother to my assistance, but we were far away——

"Our relations were continued, and the proverb is unfortunately too true, 'that the first step is the great difficulty.' Ernest rejoined his regiment, and I returned to Paris. But to my first fault I added a second, by maintaining a constant correspondence with him through a lady friend, who protected our liaison. At the beginning of the present year Ernest obtained a month's leave, which he passed in Paris. Our meetings began again by the assistance of the friend to whom I have referred; but, unfortunately, he formed the acquaintance of a fashionable young man, with whom he became very intimate. One day, after a dinner at which both drank too much champagne, Ernest told him, not only the story of our amours, but also some private details which ought to have remained a secret from everybody.

Ernest rejoined his regiment, and after his departure I noticed that at whatever hour I might go out, whether accompanied by my maid or not, I was constantly followed by a young man. One day, when my husband was out, a person called to see him.

"'Master is out,' the footman replied.

"'That is really vexatious. Do you know whether he will return soon?'

"'I do not think before dinner-time.'

"'That is more embarrassing still. If Madame Z—— were visible, I could at least intrust to her the important message which I have for her husband.'

"I was alone in the drawing-room when he was shown in, and great was my surprise at seeing the young man who so continually followed me. I rose in considerable embarrassment.

"'What do you want, sir?'

"'Madame, he said to me boldly, 'the subject of my visit must not alarm you. I love you to distraction. Your adored image is present to me night and day, and I cannot live without possessing you.'

"I was going to ring to have the audacious man turned out, when he arrested my arm by saying, in a hollow voice, 'Yes, you will be mine as you were Ernest's.'

"At this name my blood flowed back to my heart. Looking at the man with terror, I felt that my strength was leaving me, and I fell back on the sofa which was behind me. He looked at me in silence, a diabolical smile played round his mouth, for he noticed the effect which one word produced upon me; but ere long he continued—

"'I know all, madam—the stroll in the wood at your mother's country-house—your daily meetings, and a certain secret mark which only your husband ought to know. But reassure yourself; you have nothing to fear, if you will render me happy by returning my love.'

"His love! he horrified me. I was ashamed at being loved by such a villain. He doubtless noticed my disgust, for he continued—

"'Ah! you wish for war? Well, be it so; you shall have it. I terrify you, eh? You probably think that I am not so good as your Ernest? Well, I will make you pass for my mistress in the eyes of the world, and even of your husband. I know sufficient details to ruin you; and this article,' he added, as he seized a valuable bracelet which my husband had given me on my birthday, and was lying—'this article, in which is your portrait, will incontestably prove the truth of my statement, by serving me as a love-token.'

"Then he gave me a deep bow and went away. Such, sir, is the embarrassment in which I am. If you cannot get me out of the awful position, I will write my husband a letter, confessing all my faults, and then charcoal——"

"Oh, you are going too far, madame; and the position, perhaps, is not desperate as you make it. The young man who called on you is a friend of M. Ernest——"

"Yes, sir."

"And you call him——"

"Léon B——; at least that is the name by which Ernest designated him."

"Very good, madame. Calm yourself, and come and see me again in two days. Between this and then Léon will have made no attempt, and perhaps I may be so fortunate as to do something which will cause you pleasure."

When the lady had left me, I began thinking. A young man of the name of Léon B——, who only frequented the highest society, had been denounced to me as a most daring "Greek," who made his living at the German watering-places. I made inquiries; and no longer doubting my man's identity, I sent to request him to come to my office directly. Two hours after, my clerk announced him.

"What, sir!" I said to him point blank; "you are not satisfied with living at the expense of others, but must also try, by infamous means, to destroy the reputation of a lady, and rob her. You see that I know all; and I suppose you wish me to denounce you publicly, and have you constantly watched? You will at once go to Madame Z——, hand her the bracelet you stole from her—yes, sir, stole!—and you will apologize to her for the cowardly and dishonourable way in which you behaved to her. Begone! and if ever you open your lips about this matter to a soul, I warn you that I shall mercilessly denounce you."

On the next day Madame Z—— came to thank me

warmly for what I had done for her. The terrible consequences which she had fortunately escaped had produced a complete reaction in her impressionable nature, and from this moment, aware of her faults as well as her duties, she has, by exemplary conduct, expiated her sins to some extent.

CHAPTER XXIX.

SELF-CONVICTED MURDERERS.

If, in certain murdercases, the police have displayed peculiar skill, remarkable perspicacity, and inexhaustible patience in arresting the murderers, there are other cases in which the concourse of events, or an unexpected piece of information, has sufficed to enable them to detect the criminal. At times, also, the murderer has left behind him, and at each step, marks which the police only required to collect, and a traced road which they only needed to follow. Here are some instances.

On April 25th, 1836, some workmen engaged in drawing wood from the river on to the bank noticed a large bundle drifting with the current, and on the point of disappearing under a boat. Thinking it worth having, the raftsmen hastily fished up the bundle, which was artistically tied up and apparently contained wares. But great was their horror when, on opening it, they saw two female legs, the flesh of which seemed to have been torn away from the body, and the bones cleverly sawn through. These mutilated limbs were enveloped in a corn sack, which was covered with a table cloth and other linen; the whole was covered with a thick layer of straw, held together by a packing canvas fastened with cords. In a word, this bale proved, by its arrangement and shape, that it had been formed by a hand accustomed to this sort of work. Two hours after, some fishermen found in the same way a bale resembling the first, in which was a female trunk, that is to say the other part of the corpse, nailed down to a side-board door. The perpetrator of the crime had carried his derision so far as to place on his victim's chest a piece of paper bearing the inscription: "Journal of the Carnival."

These human relics, when conveyed to the Morgue, formed a body which Madame Bejou, who kept the pnblic-house "La Grosse Pipe," at the corn market, recognised as that of Dame Renaudin, called Ferrand. The information we speedily obtained led us to find that the unhappy woman had lived at No. 6, Rue des Egouts Saint Martin. Our chief Sergeant Fraudin, the agents and myself, proceeded to this house, where we learned from the other lodgers that Madame Ferrand, accompanied by a journeyman cabinet-maker of the name of L'Huissier, had moved a short time before without leaving her address, and the gossip we collected only seemed to entangle the threads which might have led to the discovery of the murderer. We were at this point, when a Madame Provost, living on the fourth floor of the house, joined us. Soon learning the nature of our visit, she addressed us in a very voluble manner.

"Gentlemen, you wish to know Ma'me Ferrand's address? Well, I will tell it to you. When she left here she would not give it to anybody, and the good creature was quite at liberty to do so. But no matter, it seemed to me queer; for when a person hides her address there is some mystery concealed. Hence, I said to myself, 'when the van arrives I will follow it at a distance,' and I did follow the van to No. 92, Rue Richelieu, where L'Huissier had the goods unloaded."

This information put an end to our uncertainty, so we hastened to the house indicated. The porter, on being questioned, told us that L'Huissier's lodging was on the fourth floor; but we had scarce got half-way up when we met his mistress, a girl of the name of Lecomte, carrying a bucket of water.

"Is Monsieur L'Huissier at home?" we asked her.

"No, gentlemen, he has gone out, and did not say when he would return."

In spite of this negative answer, Sergeant Fraudin followed the girl closely, and when she opened the door went in after. L'Huissier, who was in bed, was arrested with his mistress. This is what had previously occurred. L'Huissier, without the knowledge of Lecomte, with whom he lived in concubinage, had formed the acquaintance of Madame Ferrand. He soon formed the plan of getting hold of the comfortable furniture which she possessed, and in order to gain his end he induced her to remove by offering her a lodging at the end of the yard of his own house. When all the furniture had been deposited in the new apartment, and L'Huissier found himself alone with Madame Ferrand, he murdered her, and then separated the legs from the trunk with a saw. The operation ended, he made two packets, hired a truck, and at nine in the evening carried his sanguinary burden as far as the vicinity of the Bridge de la Concorde. Here, as the porter who helped him was in his way, he got rid of him by pretending that a vehicle would come to fetch his two bales, which he at once threw into the river.

During his trial he displayed a rough coolness, and in spite of the crushing weight of evidence, he denied to the last that he was the perpetrator of the crime. When condemned to death he mounted the scaffold with the same affected coolness which he had displayed in court. The woman was acquitted, and justly so, for her lover had formed and carried out his frightful plan without her knowledge.

On January 25, 1851, one of the keepers at the Château of Neuilly, while taking his usual morning walk round the park, noticed that his dog stopped before the hedge separating the park from the Villieris road. Urged by a very natural curiosity, the keeper went up and saw a shapeless mass lying at the bottom of the ditch, upon the blood-stained ground. As he could not distinguish exactly what it was, he resolved to go round and make certain of what he had seen. On reaching the spot he found a corpse, no longer possessing a human face, for the head had been so injured. At this moment other persons came up, and picked up here and there, one a piece of jaw containing three teeth, another the blood-stained lobe of an ear, lying by the side of a stone, which was one mass of blood. In the pockets of the victim there was not a single paper or anything to identify him with.

So soon as I was informed of the melancholy event I sent several agents to Neuilly to make inquiries. They were just going to leave when Dr. Cazaux came to inform me that his man-servant, Chaillou by name, had left his house on the previous evening for the purpose of going to Neuilly. On leaving he told the porter that he should be home late; but he did not come in at all. The agents on returning from Neuilly informed me that on the previous evening two persons who came from Paris called on the F——'s, who were employed at the Chateau; that one of them was Edward Voisy, brother of Madame F——, and belonging to the Paris fire-brigade, and the other a young man of the name of Chaillou, an intimate friend of Voisy and his family, who was footman to Dr. Cazaux, at No. 12, Rue des Saints Pères.

From this moment I could entertain no doubt; the assassin was Voisy, and the victim Chaillou. The next point was to arrest the former. It was a Sunday; a day of rest for magistrates, and there was not a soul at the Palace of Justice. I made a detailed report of the affair, which I sent to a magistrate, who at once issued warrants for the arrest of Voisy and the F——s, but the latter were set at liberty a few days after. The corpse of the unhappy Chaillou was transported to the Morgue, and recognised by Dr. Cazaux. Voisy was arrested when he went to his barracks, and was tried by court-martial and sentenced to penal servitude for life.

A man of the name of Miller, a journeyman mechanic, and native of Savoy, strong, short, and plump, like the majority of his countrymen, had had very intimate relations with a girl called Annette Legeard; but one fine day, our amorous couple, tired of one another and of their constant quarrels, broke the connecting link, and fled away in different directions. On September 20, 1851, however, about eight in the evening, Miller found himself face to face with his ex-mistress in the Rue St. Louis. The fickle Savoyard had very exaggerated notions; he wished to be eternally regretted, while Miss Annette, on the other hand, thought that the place of a lost lover ought to be filled up immediately. From these different opinions resulted a very sharp altercation, at the end of which the jealous man plunged his knife into the girl's stomach. The assassin ran off, and the victim, who had fallen bathed in her blood, was carried to an hospital, where she died shortly after.

Miller lived in the Rue de l'Homme-Armé, and had not reappeared there since the crime; his clothes and linen were still in the room. I felt persuaded that he would some day go himself, or send a porter to fetch them, and hence I only required to establish a watch in the vicinity in order to effect his arrest. But this method, apparently so simple, offered a very great difficulty. The Rue de l'Homme-Armé is excessively narrow; no vehicle can pass through it, and there is not a single shop. Such a street is most unfitted to establish a surveillance, for the agents would be too easily remarked. I therefore came to an arrangement with the porter of the house, who promised to warn his police-commissioner, no matter the hour, by day or night, if Miller came, or any other person in his name. On the next Monday, at nine in the evening, the murderer, having noticed no one in the street, entered the house and went straight up to his room. The porter did not speak to him, but went at once to warn the police-commissioner. Miller was arrested, and condemned to penal servitude for life.

Mademoiselle Ribault, drawer of designs, sixty-one years of age, engaged on the *Petit Courrier des Dames*, resided with her companion, a Mademoiselle Lebel, who was seventy-two years of age, in a modest suite of rooms at No. 1, Rue Bourbon le Château. Their peaceful existence seemed as if it would be prolonged for a lengthened period, but contrary to all human foresight it was destined to have a deplorable end. On December 31, 1850, they were both murdered at about two in the afternoon, and the assassin before escaping, seized a sum of 550 francs in gold. The circumstances were as follows. On the last day of every month, a clerk of the newspaper came to pay Mademoiselle Ribault a sum of 200 francs for her monthly work. After the clerk's visit, there was no sign of life in the rooms occupied by the old ladies. The landlady of the house rang the bell several times, but obtained no answer, and, alarmed by the unusual silence, she resolved, at eleven in the evening, on having the door broken open by a locksmith. Then, a frightful spectacle was visible; at each end of the room lay a victim, bathed in her blood. Mademoiselle Lebel had heaved her last sigh several hours before, but her mistress still gave signs of life. The latter unfortunate lady had fainted through the severe loss of blood entailed by her numerous wounds; and her limbs, already weakened by age, were to some extent paralyzed. On regaining her senses she dragged herself to the mantelpiece, and by a final sublime effort traced on the fender with a finger dipped in her own blood these few denunciatory words, which survived her and insured the punishment of the murderer: *The assassin is M. Thierry's clerk!*

The police, informed of these circumstances, at once proceeded to Montmartre, to the residence of the murderer, a man of the name of Laforcade, but he was not at home. A surveillance was then established at his lodgings, and at the office of the *Courrier des Dames*, and the murderer was arrested at the latter place during the course of the day, and taken to the prefecture. He was placed in a cell, and his first thought was to commit suicide and escape the scaffold. A piece of broken glass which he found under his bed served as the instrument, and he opened his veins; but the keepers arrived in time to save his life. Laforcade was condemned to death, and duly executed.

THE END.

Literature of Mystery and Detection

AN ARNO PRESS COLLECTION

Adams, Samuel Hopkins. **Average Jones.** [1911]

Allen, Grant. **An African Millionaire.** 1897

Arkwright, Richard. **The Queen Anne's Gate Mystery.** 1889. Two volumes in one

Benson, E[dward] F[rederic]. **The Blotting Book.** 1908

[Burgess, Gelett]. **The Master of Mysteries.** [1912]

Canler, [Louis]. **Autobiography of a French Detective From 1818 To 1858.** 1862

Claretie, Jules. **The Crime of the Boulevard.** [1897]

Collins, Wilkie. **The Queen of Hearts.** 1859

Farjeon, B[enjamin] L[eopold]. **Devlin the Barber.** 1888

[Felix, Charles]. **The Notting Hill Mystery.** [1862]

Gaboriau, Emile. **File No. 113.** 1900

Gaboriau, Emile. **The Widow Lerouge.** 1873

Green, Anna Katherine. **The Filigree Ball.** [1903]

Griffiths, Arthur [George Frederick]. **The Rome Express.** 1907

Gulik, R[obert] H[ans] van. **Dee Goong An:** Three Murder Cases Solved by Judge Dee. [1949]

Haggard, H. Rider. **Mr. Meeson's Will.** 1888

Hawthorne, Julian. **David Poindexter's Disappearance and Other Tales.** London, 1888

Hume, Fergus [Wright]. **The Mystery of a Hansom Cab.** [n. d.]

James, Henry. **The Other House.** 1896

Leblanc, Maurice. **The Exploits of Arsène Lupin.** [1907]

Leighton, Marie Connor and Robert Leighton. **Michael Dred, Detective,** 1899

Leroux, Gaston. **The Mystery of the Yellow Room.** 1908

Lowndes, [Marie Adelaide] Belloc. **The End of Her Honeymoon.** 1913

Lynch, Lawrence L. (pseud. of Emma Murdoch Van Deventer). **Dangerous Ground.** 1885

Meade, L. T. (pseud. of Elizabeth Thomasina Smith) and Clifford Halifax. **Stories From the Diary of a Doctor.** 1895

Moffett, Cleveland. **Through the Wall.** [1909]

Morrison, Arthur. **Martin Hewitt, Investigator.** [1894]

O. Henry (pseud. of William Sidney Porter). **The Gentle Grafter.** 1908

Orczy, [Emmuska]. **Lady Molly of Scotland Yard.** [1926]

Payn, James. **Lost Sir Massingberd.** [n. d.]

Pemberton, Max. **Jewel Mysteries I Have Known.** [1894]

Pidgin, Charles Felton and J. M. Taylor. **The Chronicles of Quincy Adams Sawyer, Detective.** 1912

Pinkerton, Allan. **The Expressman and the Detective.** 1875

Post, Melville Davisson. **The Strange Schemes of Randolph Mason.** [1896]

Reeve, Arthur B[enjamin]. **The Silent Bullet.** 1912

Shiel, M[atthew] P[hipps]. **Prince Zaleski.** 1895

[Simms, William Gilmore]. **Martin Faber, The Story of a Criminal;** and Other Tales. 1837. Two volumes in one

Speight, T[homas] W[ilkinson]. **Under Lock and Key.** 1869. Three volumes in one

Stevenson, Burton E[gbert]. **The Mystery of the Boule Cabinet.** 1921

Trollope, T[homas] Adolphus. **A Siren.** 1870. Three volumes in one

[Vidocq, Eugène François]. **Memoirs of Vidocq. Principal Agent of the French Police Until 1827.** 1828/1829. Four volumes in two

Warren, Samuel. **Experiences of a Barrister, and Confessions of an Attorney.** 1859. Two volumes in one

"Waters" (pseud. of William Russell). **The Experiences of a French Detective Officer** .[185?]

Whyte-Melville, G[eorge] J[ohn]. **M. Or N.** 1869. Two volumes in one